BRIGHT SPARKS
ADVENTURES IN READING COMPREHENSION

Enid Blyton's books have sold over 500 million copies and have been translated into other languages more often than any other children's author.

She wrote over 600 books and hundreds of short stories, including favourites such as The Famous Five, The Secret Seven, The Magic Faraway Tree, Malory Towers and Noddy.

Born in London in 1897, Enid lived much of her life in Buckinghamshire and adored dogs, gardening and the countryside. She died in 1968 but remains one of the world's best-loved storytellers.

Enid Blyton

BRIGHT SPARKS
ADVENTURES IN READING COMPREHENSION

hachette INDIA

First published in 2018 by Hachette India
(Registered name: Hachette Book Publishing India Pvt. Ltd)
An Hachette UK company
www.hachetteindia.com

SRD

978-93-5195-261-9

Hachette Book Publishing India Pvt. Ltd
4th & 5th Floors, Corporate Centre,
Plot No. 94, Sector 44, Gurugram 122003, India

Typeset in Garamond Lt Std 12/14 by
Manmohan Kumar, New Delhi

Printed and bound in India by
Manipal Technologies Limited, Manipal

FSC www.fsc.org
MIX
Paper from responsible sources
FSC™ C043100

CONTENTS

IT'S A MYSTERY!

CHAPTER ONE

Excerpt from *Five Have a Mystery to Solve*

Julian pointed lazily to a big notice not far off. It said 'BOATS FOR HIRE. ENQUIRE AT HUT.'

'Oh good!' said George. 'I'll go and ask. I'd *love* a good row!'

She slipped on her sandals, and went to the hut to which the sign pointed. A boy of about fifteen sat there, staring out to the sea. He looked round as George came along.

'Want a boat?' he said.

'Yes, please. How much?' asked George. 'For four of us – and a dog.'

'Three pounds an hour,' said the boy. 'Or six pounds a day. Or fifteen pounds a week. Better to take it by the week .

if you're staying here. It works out very cheap then.'

George went back to the boys and Anne. 'Shall we take the boat by the week?' she said. 'We could do lots of rowing about, and it'd be fun.'

'Right,' said Dick. 'Anyone got any money?'

'There's some in my pocket, but not enough I'm afraid,' said Julian. 'I'll go and arrange for us to have the boat tomorrow – we'll take it for a whole week. I can easily bring the money with me in the morning.'

The boat boy was very obliging. 'You can have the boat today and onwards, if you like, you needn't wait till tomorrow,' he said. '*I* know you'll bring me the money all right! So, if you'd like to have it this afternoon, it's up to you. Choose which boat you like. They're all the same. If you want to take it out at night too and do some fishing, you can – but tie it up safe, won't you?'

'Of course,' said Julian, going to look at the boats. He beckoned to the others, and they all came over.

'Any boat we like, day *or* night!' said Julian. 'Which do you fancy? *Starfish – Splasho – Adventure – Seagull – Rock-a-bye*? They all look good, sound little boats to me!'

'I'd like *Adventure*, I think,' said George, thinking that that particular boat looked sturdy, clean and sound. 'Nice name – and nice little boat!'

So *Adventure* it was!

'And a really good name for any boat of ours!' said Dick, pushing it down to the sea with Julian. 'Whoooooosh! There she goes! Steady – we want to get in! Chuck in all the clothes, George! We can dress when we feel cold.'

Soon they were all in the boat, bobbing about on the waves. Julian took the oars and pulled out to sea. Now they were in the full breeze – and a strong one it was too! 'I'm certainly not hot any more!' said George, pulling her swimming towel round her shoulders.

The tide was running out, and pulled the boat strongly out sea. Whispering Island suddenly seemed very much nearer! 'Better look out!' said George suddenly. 'We don't know if a keeper's on guard somewhere on the shore of the island. We're getting pretty near.'

But the outgoing tide swept the boat on and on towards the island, so that very soon they could see a sandy shore. Dick then took one oar, and Julian the other, and they tried to row against the tide and take the boat back into calm water.

It was no good. The tide was far too strong. Very soon the boat was quite near the shore of the island and then an enormous wave flung them right up the sand and left the boat grounded as it went back again. It slid over to one side, and they all promptly fell out!

'Whew!' said Julian. 'What a tide! I'd no idea it ran so strongly, or I'd never have brought the boat out so far.'

'What shall we do!' said Anne, rather scared. She kept looking all round for a keeper with a gun. Suppose they got into real trouble through coming right on to the island?

'I think we'll have to stay on the island till the tide turns, and we can row back on it,' said Julian. 'I can't think why that boat boy didn't warn us about the tide. I suppose he thought we knew.'

They pulled the boat a little further up on the firm

sand, took out their bundles of clothes and hid them under a bush. They walked up the beach towards a wood, thick with great trees. As they neared them, they heard a strange, mysterious sound.

'Whispering!' said George, stopping. 'The trees are *really* whispering. Listen! It's just as if they were talking to one another under their breath! No wonder it's called Whispering Island!'

'I don't like it much,' said Anne. 'It almost sounds as if they're saying nasty things about us!'

'Shooey, shooey, shooey, shooey!' said the trees, nodding towards one another as the wind shook them. 'Shooey, shooey!'

'Just the noise of whispering!' said George. 'Well – what do we do now? We'll have to wait an hour or two till the tide turns again!'

'Shall we explore?' said Dick. 'After all, we've got Timmy with us. No one is likely to attack us if they see *him*!'

'They can shoot him, can't they, if they have guns?' said George. 'If he growled one of his terrifying growls, and ran at them, showing his teeth, they'd be scared to bits and fire at him.'

'I think you're right,' said Julian, angry with himself for landing them all into what might be serious trouble. 'Keep your hand on Timmy's collar, George.'

'You know what I think?' said Dick suddenly. 'I think we ought to try and find the guards, and tell them the tide swept us on to the island quite by accident – we couldn't stop the boat surging on! We're not grown-ups, come to snoop around, so they're sure to believe us – and we'd be safe from any chasing or shooting then.'

They all looked at Julian. He nodded. 'Yes – good idea. Give ourselves up, and ask for help! After all, we hadn't any real intention of actually landing – the tide simply *threw* the boat into that sandy cove!'

So they walked up to the back of the cove and into the wood, whose whispering was very loud indeed, once they were actually among the trees. No one was to be seen. The wood was so thick that it was in parts quite difficult to clamber through. After about ten minutes of very hard walking and clambering, Julian came to a stop. He had seen something through the trees.

The others pressed behind him. Julian pointed in front, and the others saw what looked like a great grey wall, made of stone.

COMPREHENSION CHECK!

Q How is the boat boy so sure that the children will pay him the next day?

Q Why does Dick think *Adventure* is a good name for their boat?

Q Why does Anne think the trees are whispering nasty things about the Five?

Q How does Enid Blyton build excitement and tension in this excerpt? She makes you:

- ☐ laugh
- ☐ feel sad
- ☐ feel scared
- ☐ feel irritated

Q How does she achieve this effect? Give two reasons for your answer.

1. ______________________________

____

2. ______________________________

____

Q Find at least two synonyms for the following words:

OBLIGING ______________________________

ENORMOUS ______________________________

SURGE ______________________________

BECKON ______________________________

STURDY ______________________________

Use the words listed above to make sentences.

____

____

____

____

____

____

____

Are these statements right or wrong? Tick your choice. Then, write the correct answer in the space provided.

A The boat gets stranded on the island because of a storm.

☐ RIGHT ☐ WRONG

B The boat boy gives *Adventure* to the Famous Five for free.

☐ RIGHT ☐ WRONG

C On Whispering Island the trees seem to whisper to each other.

☐ RIGHT ☐ WRONG

D Julian decides that everyone should swim back to the shore rather than risk getting caught.

☐ RIGHT ☐ WRONG

Have you ever been on a boat? Hop on and name its parts.

Bow
Oars
Hull
Stern

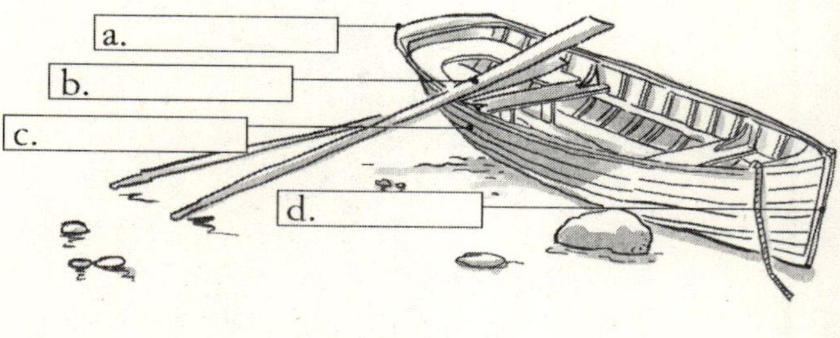

Describe the following characters in two sentences each.		
ANNE	GEORGE	THE BOAT BOY

In the excerpt, the trees nod 'Shooey shooey shooey' at one another. Shooey is a sound word. When a word imitates the sound of something that it is trying to describe, it is called onomatopoeia (say aw-no-mat-oh-pee-ya). You might want to try saying that out loud and get your tongue tied in knots.

Now use 'Shooey shooey shooey' to make a nonsense rhyme of four lines. A nonsense rhyme is just a fun rhyme that doesn't have to make sense. The first line of the poem has been done for you.

'Gooey gooey gooey,' shrieked Mom,

SCAMPER AND TIMMY MAKE MISCHIEF!

CHAPTER TWO

Pets were important characters in many of Enid Blyton's books – there were dogs, of course, but also monkeys and parrots. Here are two excerpts from two different series that feature pets.

Excerpt from *Secret Seven Adventure*

It was really Scamper the spaniel who found the biggest clue of all. He was with them, of course, sniffing around eagerly, very interested in the curious round marks. Then he suddenly began to bark loudly.

Everyone looked at him. 'What's up, Scamper?' said Peter.

Scamper went on barking. The Seven felt a bit scared, and looked hastily round, half afraid that there might be somebody hidden in the bushes!

Scamper had his head up, and was barking quite madly. 'Stop it,' said Peter, exasperated. 'Tell us what you're barking at, Scamper! Stop it, I say.'

Scamper stopped. He gave Peter a reproachful look and then gazed up above the children's heads. He began to bark again.

Everyone looked up, to see what in the world the spaniel was barking at. And there, caught neatly on the twig of a tree, was a cap!

'Look at that!' said Peter, astonished. 'A cap! Could it belong to the thief?'

'Well, if it does, why in the world did he throw his cap up there?' said Janet. 'It's not a thing that thieves usually do – throw their caps up into trees and leave them!'

The cap was far too high to reach. It was almost as high up as the top of the wall! John the gardener went to get a stick to knock it down.

'It could only have got up there by being thrown,' said George. 'So it doesn't really seem as if it could have belonged to the thief. He really wouldn't go throwing his cap about like that, leaving such a great clue!'

'No. You're right, I'm afraid,' said Peter. 'It can't be his cap. It must be one that some tramp threw over the wall some time or other.'

John came back with a bamboo stick. He jerked the cap off the twig and Scamper pounced on it at once.

'Drop it, Scamper; drop it!' ordered Peter, and Scamper dropped it, looking hurt. Hadn't he spotted the cap himself? Then at least he might be allowed to throw it up into the air and catch it!

The Seven looked at the dirty old cap. It was made of tweed, and at one time must

have shown a rather startling check pattern – but now it was so faded that it was difficult to even see the pattern. Janet looked at it in disgust.

'Ugh! What a tatty old cap! I'm sure that some tramp had finished with it and thrown it over the wall – and it just stuck up there on that tree branch. I'm sure it isn't a clue at all.'

'I think you're right,' said Colin, turning the cap over and over in his hands. 'We might as well chuck it over into Little Thicket. It's no use to us. Bad luck, Scamper – you thought you'd found a thumping big clue!'

Excerpt from *Five Are Together Again*

But Timmy went on growling. Then he suddenly stood still and sniffed hard. He gave an excited whimper and pulled away from George, jumping into the bushes – and out came, not a snake, but Mischief, Tinker's bright-eyed little monkey!

He at once leapt on to the dog's broad back, put his little monkey fingers under Timmy's collar, and chattered in delight. Timmy nearly dislocated his neck trying to twist his head round to lick him!

'Mischief!' cried everyone at once, in real delight. 'You've come to welcome us!'

And the little monkey, jabbering away excitedly in monkey language, leapt first on to George's shoulder, and then on to Julian's. He pulled Julian's hair, twisted his right ear round, and then leapt from him to Dick, and on to Anne's shoulder. He cuddled into her neck, his eyes bright and brown, looking very happy.

'Oh! *Isn't* he pleased to see us again!' said Anne, delighted. 'Mischief, where's Tinker?'

Mischief jumped off Anne's shoulder and scampered down the drive as if he quite understood all that Anne had said. The children raced after him – and then a stentorian voice suddenly roared at them from one side of the drive.

'What are you doing here? Clear out! This is private ground. I'll fetch the police. Clear OUT!'

The Five stopped still in fright – and then Julian saw who it was – Professor Hayling! He stepped forward at once. 'Good afternoon, sir,' he said. 'I hope we didn't disturb you, but you did tell my aunt we could come here.'

'Your aunt? Who's your aunt? I don't know any aunt!' roared the Professor. 'You're sightseers, that's what you are! Come to pry into my work, just because there was a piece about it in some silly paper! You're the third lot today. Clear off, I tell you – and take that dog too. How DARE you!'

'But – don't you really know us?' said Julian, very startled. 'You came to stay at our house, you know, and...'

'Stuff and nonsense! I haven't been away for years!' shouted the Professor. Mischief, the monkey, was so frightened that he leapt away into the bushes, making a funny little crying noise.

'I hope he fetches Tinker,' said Julian, in a low voice to Dick. 'The Professor has forgotten who we are, and why we've come. Let's retreat a bit.'

But as they went cautiously back up the steep path, followed by the angry Professor, a loud voice hailed them, and Tinker came racing up with Mischief on his shoulder, clinging to his hair. So the little monkey had gone to fetch him. 'Good for *him*!' thought Julian, pleased.

'Dad! Don't yell at our friends like that!' cried Tinker, dancing about in front of his angry father. 'You asked them here yourself, you know you did!'

'I DID NOT!' said the Professor. 'Who are they?'

'Well, George, that girl, is the daughter of Mr Kirrin and the others are his niece and nephews. And that's their dog, Timmy. And you asked them all here because Mr and Mrs Kirrin are in quarantine for scarlet fever,' shouted Tinker, still dancing about in front of his father.

'Stop jigging about like that,' said the Professor, crossly. '*I* don't remember asking them. I would have told Jenny the maid, if I had.'

'You did tell her!' shouted Tinker, still jigging about, with Mischief the monkey jigging too in delight. 'She's already made up the beds. I helped her. She's angry because you left your breakfast and now it's almost dinner-time. She's cleared it away.'

'Bless us all – so *that's* why I feel so hungry and cross!' said Professor Hayling, and he began to laugh. He had a tremendous laugh, and the children couldn't help laughing too. What an odd fellow – so brainy, such a fine scientist – with the most enormous amount of knowledge in his head – and yet no memory for such ordinary things as breakfast and visitors and telephone calls.

'It was just a misunderstanding, sir,' said Julian, politely. 'It was very, very kind of you to invite us here when we can't be at home because of the scarlet fever. We'll try not to be a nuisance, and if there's anything we can do to help you, please ask us. We'll make as little noise as possible, and keep out of your way, of course.'

COMPREHENSION CHECK!

Q In the first excerpt, Scamper the spaniel discovers what the Seven at first think is a clue. In the second excerpt, what does Timmy discover?

Q In the first excerpt, whose dog do you think Scamper is? Why do you think so?

Q Dogs are often used by the police in detective work. What are the qualities that make dogs good find-outers?

Describe Mischief the monkey in three sentences using at least one adjective in each sentence. Remember, an adjective is a word that describes a noun. Give examples from the excerpt to support your answer. For example, *Mischief the monkey is quick because he jumps from Timmy to Anne to George, then Julian, before tearing off to fetch Tinker.*

1.

2.

3.

Q The word 'curious' has two meanings. Write them down and make a sentence for each of those meanings.

1.

2.

Q The word 'cross' also has two meanings. Write them down and make a sentence for each of those meanings.

1.

2.

There are different kinds of dogs. For example, Scamper is a spaniel. Write down five other dog types you know.

MATCH THE FOLLOWING

Draw lines to match the characters to the adjectives that describe them best.

CHARACTERS	ADJECTIVES
Scamper	respectful
Mischief	forgetful
Julian	exasperated
Professor	naughty
Tinker	excited

9789351952619 Adventures in Reading Text:F.4

AMAZING MAZE

Follow Mischief's tail to find Timmy!

GONE MISSING!

CHAPTER THREE

Excerpt from *Secret Seven Mystery*

Peter explained everything clearly.

'The girl's name is Elizabeth Mary Wilhemina Sonning,' he said. 'Her parents live abroad, and she is a weekly boarder at school and spends her weekends with an aunt. She has a brother who is away in France. She was accused of stealing money from her teacher's desk, and when the police went to speak to her aunt about it, she ran away.'

'What was she dressed in?' asked Pam.

'School uniform,' said Peter. 'Here's her photograph in it. Ordinary navy school coat, navy felt hat with school band round it, ordinary shoes, and socks. It says here that she wore a grey skirt underneath, with a white blouse – well, really she's dressed just like Janet and Pam and Barbara when they're at school, it seems to me!'

'She may have taken some other clothes with her,' said Jack. 'Her Sunday coat or something.'

'No. Her aunt said that no other clothes were missing – only the ones she went in,' said Peter. 'You may be sure the aunt would look carefully, because it would be difficult to spot the girl if she were not in her school uniform.'

'Where's the description of what she's like?' asked Janet. 'It was in the evening paper last night, Peter.'

'Oh yes. Here it is,' said Peter, and began to read out loud, "Elizabeth can be recognized by her mass of soft, dark, curly hair, her brown eyes, straight eyebrows, and scar down one arm. She is tall for her age, and strong. She swims well and is fond of horses." Well – there you are – do you think you'd spot her if you saw her?'

'We might,' said Colin, doubtfully. 'But lots of girls have dark, curly hair and brown eyes. If only the girl would wear short sleeves we might spot the scar – but that's the one thing she will certainly hide!'

'How do we set about looking for her?' asked George. 'Do we bike over to Belling Village and hunt all over the place?'

'That's what we've got to discuss,' said Peter. 'I don't actually think that just biking up and down the streets is going to be the slightest good – Elizabeth will be sure to find a hiding place. She won't wander about in the daytime, I imagine – she'll lie low.'

'Where?' asked Pam.

'How do *I* know?' said Peter who thought that Pam was sometimes very silly. 'Use your brains, Pam. Where would *you* hide if you ran away from home?'

'In a barn,' said Pam.

'In the woods under a thick bush,' said George.

'Wuff, wuff, wuff-wuff,' said Scamper, wagging his tail.

'What did you suggest – in a *kennel?*' said Peter. 'Thank you, Scamper – quite a good idea of yours!'

Everyone laughed, and Scamper looked pleased.

'I thought it would be sensible if we thoroughly explored Belling Village and round about,' said Peter. 'If Elizabeth has already been *seen* in Belling, she must be hiding *some*where near. I expect the police have already hunted pretty well everywhere, but we know better where to look than they do – because we know where *we'd* hide if we wanted to – but they wouldn't. Grown-ups seem to forget the things they did when they were young.'

'Yes, they do,' said George. 'But I *never* shall. I'm determined not to. What about the grandmother, Peter? Should one of us go see her, do you think? She might have something helpful to say.'

'Yes, I think that's a good idea,' said Peter, considering it.

'Bags, *I* don't go,' said Pam at once. 'I wouldn't know what to say. I should just stand there and look silly.'

'Well, you'd find *that* quite easy,' said Colin, and Pam scowled at him.

'Now just you tell me what you – ' she began, but Peter stopped the argument before it began.

'Shut up, you two. Jack and I will go, probably. And listen – there is another thing we might do.'

'What?' asked everyone.

'Well, this girl is fond of horses, it seems. We might go to the two or three stables we know of and see if any girl has been seen hanging around. She might even try to get a job at one.'

'That's a *good* idea,' said Janet, warmly. 'Well – there seems to be quite a lot we can do, Peter.'

COMPREHENSION CHECK!

Q Here is a description of Elizabeth. There are mistakes in it. Could you correct them so that we can help the newspaper get their facts right?

Elizabeth can be recognized by her mass of soft, brown, curly hair, her grey eyes, straight eyebrows, and a scar on her shoulder. She is small for her age, and strong. She runs well and is fond of cycling.

Fill in the blanks by selecting the correct phrase from the ones provided below.

they'd know where a young girl may hide better than grown-ups would
a missing girl
stolen money
the scar on her arm
she wouldn't know what to say to her

a. In this excerpt the Seven set out to solve the mystery of

____

____

b. The police believe that Elizabeth has ______________________________

____

____

c. Elizabeth has dark hair and brown eyes like many other girls, so the Seven think the easiest way to make her out is by looking for ______________________________

____

____

d. The Seven think that they might have better success than the police in finding Elizabeth because ______________________________

____

____

e. Pam doesn't want to be the one to visit the grandmother because ______________________________

____

____

CROSSWORD FUN

Find synonyms for the following words in the crossword grid and write them next to the words in the space provided.

P	Q	R	S	D	P	Q	R	S	T	P	Q	R	S	T	P	R	R	S
Q	R	S	T	I	P	Q	R	S	T	Q	R	S	T	T	P	Q	R	S
R	S	D	E	S	E	R	T	E	D	R	S	S	S	T	P	Q	R	Q
S	T	P	S	A	P	Q	R	S	T	S	T	P	S	T	P	Q	R	S
P	Q	R	S	G	P	Q	R	S	T	P	Q	R	T	E	N	A	N	T
Q	R	S	T	R	P	Q	R	S	T	P	R	S	H	P	Q	S	T	P
R	S	S	S	E	P	Q	R	S	T	P	S	T	I	P	R	S	T	T
S	T	T	S	E	P	Q	R	S	D	P	T	R	C	P	Q	R	S	H
T	P	Q	R	M	P	Q	S	H	E	D	Q	R	K	P	R	S	T	I
P	Q	R	S	E	P	Q	R	S	B	P	C	P	E	P	Q	R	S	N
Q	R	S	T	N	K	I	N	G	A	B	O	U	T	P	T	R	S	K
R	S	T	P	T	P	Q	R	S	T	P	M	P	Q	R	R	S	P	I
S	T	P	S	T	Q	B	P	Q	E	P	P	Q	R	S	S	T	Q	N
T	P	Q	S	P	R	L	P	Q	R	S	L	R	S	T	T	T	R	G
P	Q	R	S	T	S	A	P	Q	R	S	E	S	T	P	Q	R	S	A
Q	R	S	S	T	T	M	P	Q	R	S	T	T	P	Q	R	S	T	B
R	S	T	S	T	R	E	S	O	L	V	E	D	Q	R	S	T	P	O
S	T	R	S	T	P	Q	R	S	T	P	L	P	R	S	P	Q	R	U
T	P	Q	R	T	P	Q	R	S	T	P	Y	P	S	T	Q	R	S	T

ACROSS

1. boarder ____________
2. determined ____________
3. considering ____________
4. barn ____________
5. empty ____________

DOWN

1. argument ____________
2. discuss ____________
3. accuse ____________
4. thoroughly ____________
5. copse ____________

AN IMPORTANT MEETING

CHAPTER FOUR

Excerpt from *First Term at Malory Towers*

'New girls must go to see the Head Mistress after breakfast,' announced Miss Potts. 'There are three in the first form, two in the second form, and one in the fourth. You can all go together. Join us in the assembly room for Prayers later. Pamela, will you take the new girls to the Head, please?'

Pamela, head-girl of North Tower House, rose. The new girls stood up, Darrell among them. They followed Pamela. She took them out of the door that let into the Court, and then in through another door set in the building that ran between East and North Tower.

The Head Mistress's rooms were there, and so was the San. or sanatorium, where any sick girl went.

They came to a door painted a deep cream colour. Pamela knocked.

A low voice said, 'Come in!'

Pamela opened the door. 'I've brought the new girls to you, Miss Grayling,' she said.

'Thank you, Pamela,' said the low voice again, and Darrell saw a grey-haired woman sitting at a desk, writing. She had a calm, unwrinkled face, eyes that were startlingly blue, and a very firm mouth. Darrell felt frightened of this calm, low-voiced Head Mistress, and hoped she would never have to be sent to her for misbehaviour!

The new girls stood in a row before the Head, and Miss Grayling looked at them all closely. Darrell felt herself going red, she couldn't imagine why. Her knees felt a bit wobbly too. She hoped Miss Grayling wouldn't ask her any questions, for she was sure she wouldn't be able to say a word!

Miss Grayling asked them their names, and spoke a few words to each girl. Then she addressed them all solemnly.

'One day you will leave school and go out into the world as young women. You should take with you eager minds, kind hearts, and a will to help. You should take with you a good understanding of many things, and a willingness to accept responsibility and show yourselves as women to be loved and trusted. All these things you will be able to learn at Malory Towers – if you will. I do not count as our successes those who have won scholarships and passed exams, though these are good things to do. I count as our successes those who learn to be good-hearted and kind, sensible and trustable, good, sound women the world can lean on. Our failures are those who do not learn these things in the years they are here.'

These words were spoken so gravely and solemnly that Darrell hardly breathed. She immediately longed to be one of Malory Towers' successes.

'It is easy for some of you to learn these things, and hard for others. But easy or hard, they must be learnt if you are to be happy, after you leave here, and if you are to bring happiness to others.'

There was a pause. Then Miss Grayling spoke again, in a lighter tone. 'You will all get a tremendous lot out of your time at Malory Towers. See that you give a lot back!'

'Oh!' said Darrell, surprised and pleased, quite forgetting that she had thought she wouldn't be able to speak a word, 'that's exactly what my father said to me when he said goodbye, Miss Grayling!'

'Did he?' said Miss Grayling, looking with smiling eyes at the eager little girl. 'Well, as you have parents who think in that way, I imagine you will be one of the lucky ones, and will find that the things I have been speaking of will be easy to learn. Perhaps one day Malory Towers will be proud of you.'

A few more words and the girls were told to go. Very much impressed they walked out of the room. Not even Gwendoline said a word. Whatever they might do, in the years to come at Malory Towers, each girl wanted, at that moment, to do her best. Whether or not that wish would last, depended on the girl.

Then they went to the Assembly Hall for Prayers, found their places, and waited for Miss Grayling to come to the platform.

Soon the words of a hymn sounded in the big hall. The first day of term had begun. Darrell sang with all her might, happy and excited. What a lot she would have to tell her mother when she wrote!

COMPREHENSION CHECK!

Q Why does Darrell feel nervous before the Head Mistress?

Q A little later Darrell does not feel so scared anymore. Why do you think she is able to relax?

Q Why do children sometimes feel afraid of their teachers?

Write one antonym and two synonyms for the words given below. An antonym is a word or phrase opposite in meaning to another word or phrase in the same language. A synonym is a word or a phrase that means exactly or nearly the same as another word or phrase.

	ANTONYM	SYNONYM 1	SYNONYM 2
EAGER			
SOLEMN			
SUCCESS			

Why do you think the Head Mistress values 'good understanding of many things, and a willingness to accept responsibility and show yourselves as women to be loved and trusted', over winning scholarships and passing exams?

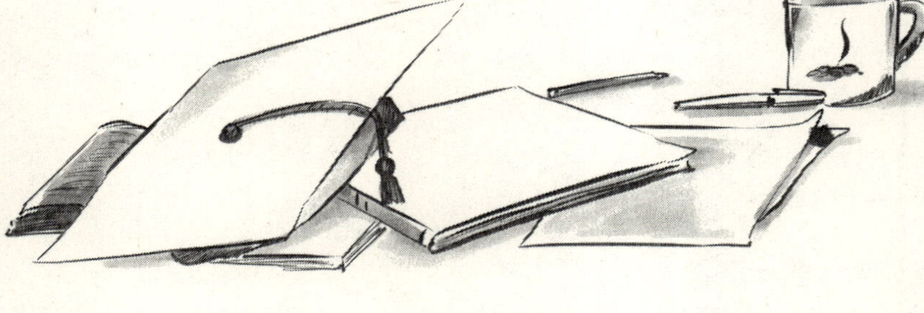

Pretend you are Darrell and write a short letter to your mother about your meeting with Miss Grayling. In your letter describe the Head Mistress and talk about her message for the new girls at Malory Towers.

Dear Mum,

Now pretend you are the Head Mistress and make a short note in your diary about young Darrell. Your note should have at least five sentences.

March

28 Wednesday

In the word puzzle below, you will find the following synonyms for the word calm:

SERENE, PACIFIC, PEACEFUL, STILL, TRANQUIL, QUIET

Circle the words as you find them.

M	A	S	C	I	E	N	T	I	S	T	O	E	K
O	M	D	B	K	O	O	B	C	I	M	O	C	D
G	C	I	F	I	C	A	P	S	P	R	H	A	Y
O	W	L	E	O	N	A	R	D	Q	U	I	E	T
S	C	N	A	D	S	E	T	L	E	H	B	S	I
E	A	D	V	A	I	E	R	J	S	H	I	P	S
D	D	O	D	T	Y	P	A	O	O	O	G	E	R
C	Y	E	S	K	N	R	N	A	L	W	B	A	E
E	N	S	E	C	C	E	Q	N	N	A	A	C	V
A	P	E	R	N	Y	H	U	E	G	R	N	E	I
Z	T	I	E	O	L	O	I	T	H	O	G	F	N
E	C	N	N	I	C	S	L	N	C	T	N	U	U
A	G	R	E	P	Y	S	H	E	L	D	O	L	P
E	E	N	T	S	T	I	L	L	N	T	I	S	T

Enid Blyton

FIT TO BE KING!

CHAPTER FIVE

Excerpt from *The Mystery of the Missing Necklace*

Fatty was preparing himself very earnestly for Tuesday night. He knew how important it was, and he also knew that, unless all his details were absolutely perfect, he might be in considerable danger.

He and the others spent a long time in the waxworks, much to the surprise of the red-headed boy, for it was very hot in there, and not many people visited the little hall these blazing days.

But Fatty had to study the figure of Napoleon very carefully indeed. He meant to get into the hall somehow on Tuesday evening, and dress himself up in Napoleon's clothes. Would they fit him? He asked Daisy what she thought.

'Yes, I should think they'd fit you very well,' she said, she said, considering first Napoleon and then Fatty. 'You had better take a few safety pins in case something doesn't quite meet. The hat will be fine – just your size, I should think. What about hair, Fatty?'

'I can manage that all right,' said Fatty. 'I rather think my own will do, if I smarm it down a bit, and pull a few pieces out in front, like old Napoleon has got. And, er – I don't know what you think – but – er – I'm not really unlike Napoleon in features, am I?'

The others stared at him. 'Well,' said Pip honestly, 'I can't see any likeness at all. Not the slightest.'

'Do you want to look like Napoleon?' said Bets in surprise. 'I don't think he looks very nice, really. And I don't like those men who go about thinking they want to conquer the whole world. Napoleon must have been very brainy, of course, and you're brainy, Fatty. But, except that you're brainy, I don't see that you're very like Napoleon.'

Fatty gave it up. He stared once more at the figure of Napoleon in its grand uniform, cocked hat, medals, epaulettes, and stars. It was a fine uniform and Fatty was longing to get into it. Well, he hadn't got long to wait now.

He tried to memorize exactly at what angle Napoleon wore his hat, exactly how he held his hands, exactly how he stared so blankly in front of him. Napoleon fortunately stood in the very front row of figures, so Fatty, as Napoleon, would be able to hear and see everything very well indeed. A little shiver went down his back when he thought of standing there, perfectly still, listening to the plans of the gang, and memorizing their appearance.

It was a very bold idea indeed. Not one of the other Find-Outers would have dared to do it. But Fatty, of course, would dare anything. Bets thought that he wouldn't even turn a hair if he met a roaring lion, the kind she met in her bad dreams, and which scared her terribly. Fatty would probably speak to it kindly and pat it, and the lion would lie down and roll over for Fatty to tickle it on its tummy – like Buster did!

The red-headed boy, curious at their sudden interest in Napoleon, came over.

'What's exciting you about him?' he said. 'Who is he? Oh – Napoleon. What was he? Some sort of soldier?'

'Don't you know?' said Bets in astonishment. 'Didn't you learn history at school?'

'I've never been to school,' said the red-headed boy. 'I belong to the Fair, and us kids hardly ever go to school unless we have to. We move about from place to place, you see, and before we're popped into some school, we're moved on again. I can read, but I can't write.'

'Why are you in the waxwork show?' asked Fatty. 'Does this hall belong to the Fair people?'

'Oh no – they've only hired it,' said the boy. 'The waxworks belong to my uncle. He's the fellow that runs the hoopla. I used to help him with that, but now I have to do the waxworks, and it's jolly dull.'

Fatty wondered if any of the Fair people were in the gang of thieves. Well, he'd know on Tuesday night.

MAD SCRAMBLE

A number of words have exchanged places in the sentences given below. Could you put them back where they actually belong and rewrite the sentences in the space provided so that they make sense again?

a) Fatty was preparing himself very considerably for Tuesday night. He knew how absolutely it was, and he also knew that, unless all his details were earnestly perfect, he might be in important danger.

b) He tried to blankly exactly at what angle Napoleon wore his hat, exactly how he held his memorize, exactly how he stared so hands in front of him.

c) It was a very dared idea indeed. Not one of the other Find-Outers would have turn to do it. But Fatty, of course, would dare anything. Bets thought that he wouldn't even bold a hair if he met a roaring lion, the kind she met in her bad terribly, and which scared her dreams.

DEALING WITH FEELINGS

Imagine you are Fatty. Circle the words you might use to describe how you are feeling about your upcoming assignment. All these words describe emotions and moods. Remember that it is sometimes possible to feel opposing emotions. For example, one might feel excited and happy but also excited and scared at the same time.

ANGRY **EXCITED** **UNHAPPY** **AMAZED**

ANXIOUS **BORED** **CONFIDENT**

DEVASTATED **EAGER** **OPTIMISTIC**

SCARED **DEPRESSED** **SHOCKED** **CALM**

WORD JUMBLE

All the words in this jumble can be found in the excerpt. Make a note of the circled letters to get the answer to this puzzle and write it in the space provided.

Enid Blyton did not write HISTORY, or CHEMISTRY, or anything about GEOMETRY or TRIGONOMETRY. But she could certainly write a good ____________________!

Desmal

Sredam

Ermmozie

Eltcohs

Fesyat

Mutym

Yarbin

FACT CHECK!

The red-headed boy doesn't know much about Napoleon Bonaparte. Can you help him learn five things about the famous French monarch? Go online and search away! Psst... his birthday is the same date as India's Independence Day, but hundreds of years before!

CAT AND MOUSE

CHAPTER SIX

Excerpt from *The Mystery of the Strange Bundle*

'I'm going to hide at the other end of the road,' said Goon. 'In case he spots me. He's scared of me, dead scared. If he so much as sees the lamp on my bike, he'll run for miles. And I want to get my hands on him, see? Now, when you see him coming, you take up one of your red lamps and swing it slowly to and fro in your hands. I'll be along at once, while you're talking to him.'

'All right,' said Willie resignedly. What with people talking about sleepwalking uncles and red slippers and bad lots and swinging lamps, Willie was fed up. He'd never

get down to a nice little snooze tonight, that was certain!

Mr Goon disappeared on his bicycle. He went to the far end of the river road, got off, and hid under a tree, his bicycle beside him. Ah, he'd catch that big boy on his way back! He'd have to come back that way, because the river barred his way at the other end of the road!

Fatty debated what to do. Should he cut down to the river, make his way across somebody's back garden and cut into the road that ran parallel with this? Or should he play a little trick on Goon?

He decided on the trick. Goon deserved one after saying that Fatty was dead scared of him! Fatty began to get to work quickly. He blackened his face with dirt. He twisted his cap the other way round, with the peak now shading his eyes. He put a white handkerchief around his neck instead of the scarf. He took off his moustache but left in his awful teeth.

He felt about on the waste piece of ground nearby. Was there anything he could use in his trick. His hand fell upon an old sack. Good – just the thing! Fatty groped about among the rubbish left by the road-menders and came upon pieces of brick and stone. He quickly slid them into the sack until it was half-full. It was very heavy.

He made his way back to the road and skirted round to the back of the watchman. Then he walked slowly by him, half-bent under the sack.

The watchman saw him, but his bleary old eyes couldn't make out who it was. He stared hard, in doubt, wishing the moon would come out from behind a cloud. He decided that whoever it was looked decidedly suspicious. It wouldn't do any harm to swing the red lamp to and fro!

He picked it up, turned himself towards Mr Goon, and swung the lamp slowly. Fatty grinned as he saw it out of the corner of his eye. He plodded on slowly, bent under the sack. If ever anyone looked like a suspicious person at that moment, Fatty did!

Mr Goon saw the swinging lamp, and came quickly down the road, keeping to the shadows, his rubber-soled shoes making no noise. He tried to see if Fatty was there, talking to the watchman. But to his great annoyance, when he got to the little hut there was no one there but Willie!

'Where is he? Why did you swing your lamp? He's not here!' said Goon, exasperated.

'I see a very suspicious chap shuffling down the river road,' said Wille. 'Not the chap as you wanted, but someone you'd like to get your hands on, I don't doubt. A real suspicious chap. And carrying a heavy sack too. You'd like to know what's in that sack, I reckon!'

'Ho! It certainly sounds bad,' said Goon, thinking that if he couldn't get his hands on Fatty, it would be satisfactory to get them on to someone else. 'What direction did he go in?'

'Yonder,' said Willie, nodding. And yonder went Goon, keeping to the shadows, tracking down Fatty and the suspicious sack. Fatty took a quick look back. Good! Goon was on his trail! He would lead him a nice little dance!

Down to the river plodded Fatty, and came to where the waves were silvery with moonlight. He turned down the towing-path that led to the small jetty nearby, and Goon followed stealthily, breathing so hard that Fatty could hear him.

Fatty walked slowly, shuffling one foot after the other, like an old, old man. He coughed mournfully as he went, a horrible hollow cough. He suddenly stopped and put down his sack as if it was too heavy. Goon stopped too.

Fatty heaved the sack on to his shoulder again, and set off once more on his way to the jetty. He stopped suddenly again when he was almost there and put the sack down once more, with a groan. Goon also stopped suddenly. He was very curious now. What was the old man doing with such a heavy sack? Where was he going? What was in the sack? Had he some accomplice he was meeting? Goon began to feel quite excited.

Fatty hoisted the sack on his back once again and went on his way. He came to the little wooden jetty. Moonlit water splashed against it. Fatty went on to the jetty and sat down with his sack as if to rest.

Now was Goon's chance! He emerged from the shadows and strode heavily up to the jetty, a big figure in the moonlight.

'Now then,' he began. 'What's your name? And what have you got in that sack?'

'Bricks and stones,' said Fatty truthfully, in a sad, weary, old-man voice.

COMPREHENSION CHECK!

Q Why does Fatty decide to play a trick on Goon?

Q What does Goon ask Willie to do when he sees Fatty?

Q Why does Willie move the lamp to and fro even though he's not sure the figure he's seen is Fatty?

Q What does Fatty do to make himself look like an old man?

Q From the excerpt, pick out two phrases to show how Goon tries to keep himself hidden from Fatty. For example, *keeping to the shadows.*

1. ____________________

2. ____________________

Q The words *decide* and *decidedly* have completely different meanings. Look up the dictionary to find out what they are. Find out what they are and make a sentence each with the two words.

1. ______________________________

____

____

2. ______________________________

____

____

Q Let's try one more! The words *resigned* and *resignedly* also have completely different meanings. Find out what the meanings are and make a sentence each with the two words.

1. ______________________________

____

____

2. ______________________________

____

____

Stick a photo of yourself here. Use a sketch pen to draw a disguise for yourself and turn into a completely different person!

A FEAST FOR FIVE

CHAPTER SEVEN

Excerpt from *Five Get into a Fix*

And away they went, whistling. It was fun to have a day all to themselves, just the two of them, together!

They took the snowy path and began to climb up the slope of the mountain. The sun was now melting the snow a little, so they could make out the path fairly easily. Then they discovered that big black stones marked the way here and there – a guide to the farmer and his men, when the snow covered the path and everything!

The view was magnificent. As they climbed higher, they could see the tops of more and more hills, all of which sparkled snowy-white in the pale January sun. 'I *say* – if only we had a bit more snow what tobogganing we could have down these slopes,' said Dick, longingly. 'I wish I'd brought my skis this morning – the snow is deep enough for them down that hill – we'd whizz along like lightning!'

They were glad when they at last came to the little hut or chalet that old Mrs Jones had spoken about. After two hours' climbing it was nice to think of having something to eat, and a good rest!

'It's quite a place,' said Julian, slipping the key into the lock. 'A little wooden house, with windows and all!'

He opened the door and went inside. Yes – it was a very fine little place indeed, with bunk beds let into the wooden walls, a stove for heating – and cupboards full of crockery – and tins of food! The two boys had the same idea at once, and swung round to one another.

'Couldn't we stay here – on our own? George would love it too,' said Julian, putting into words what Dick was already thinking. Oh – if only they *could*!

***

The boys were tired, but not too tired to examine the little hut thoroughly – though it really was more like a one-roomed house. It faced across the deep valley, and the sun shone straight into it. Julian opened cupboard after cupboard, exclaiming in delight.

'Bedding! Towels! Crockery – and cutlery! And look at these tins of food – and bottles of orangeade and the rest! My word, people who came to stay at Magga Glen in the summer must have a fantastic time!'

'We could light the stove to heat the room,' suggested Dick, pulling the oil-stove into the middle of the room.

'No. We don't need to,' said Julian. 'The sun is pouring in and it really isn't cold here. We could wrap ourselves round in rugs from that cupboard if we want to.'

'Do you think we'd be allowed to come up here, instead of living down at the farm?' said Dick, opening a tin of ham with a tin-opener that hung on a nail by the cupboard. 'It's so *much* nicer to be quite on our own and independent! George would simply love it!'

'Well we can *ask*,' said Julian, taking the cap off a bottle of orangeade. 'Can we find some biscuits to eat with this ham? Oh yes – here are some cream-cracker biscuits. I say – I'm really ravenous!'

***

'Julian! Come and wash, I tell you – you don't want to miss your meal, do you?' Julian groaned and dragged his feet up the stone stairway. But once he had sluiced himself in cold water, he felt much better, and very hungry indeed. So did Dick.

They went downstairs, feeling much fresher and were delighted to see that Mrs Jones had been in and laid the table. They went to see what there was for their high tea.

'Pork-pie – home-made of course,' said Dick. 'And what's this – golly, it's a cheese! How enormous! Smell it, Julian – it's enough to make you start eating straight away! And more of that home-made bread! Can't we start?'

'No – there are new-laid boiled eggs to begin with,' said Anne, with a laugh. 'And an apple pie and cream to end with. So I hope you really *are* hungry, you two!'

Mrs Jones came in with a pot of hot tea. She smiled at the boys as she set the big brown teapot down on the table. 'Have you had a nice day up in the mountain?' she said. 'You look fine, both of you. Did you find the hut all right?'

COMPREHENSION CHECK!

Many times, writers use weather to set the mood. In the excerpts above it is winter, but it's not gloomy and grey as you can see! Pick out words and phrases to show how winter can be the opposite of lonely and blue. The first one has been done for you:

a) The sun was now melting the snow.

b) ______________________________

____

c) ______________________________

____

d) ______________________________

____

e) ______________________________

____

Enid Blyton is quite famous for keeping her readers on the edge of hunger! Here is a table full of empty dishes. Fill it up with food from the excerpts you just read and label the dishes so that whoever comes after you can have a jolly good meal too!

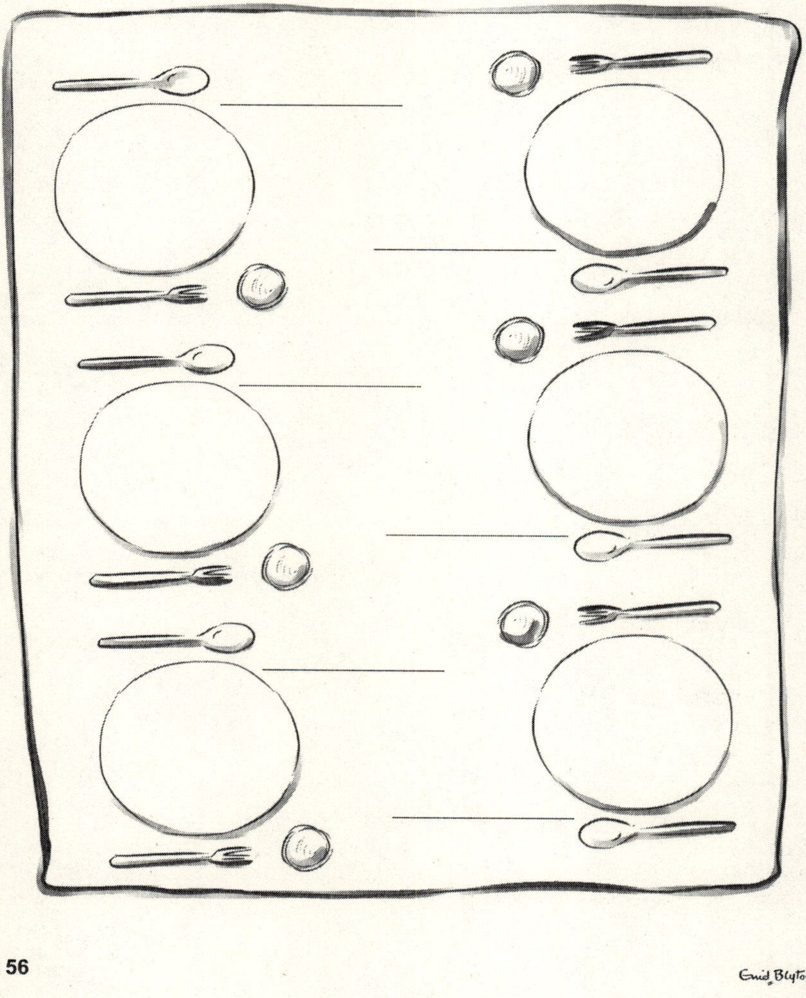

Let's have some action! Fill in the blanks with verbs. The first and last letter of each verb has been provided.

a) W______________________G like the two boys, setting off on a climb up the mountain

b) T______________________G like the children could have, down the slopes

c) E______________________G, like Julian discovering goodies in the cupboard

d) M______________________G like the snow in the sun

e) S______________________G, like the key did into the lock

There are many types of houses. A chalet is a small hut that you will find on the Swiss Alps. Many of us in cities live in flats or apartments. Name five kinds of houses that people in different parts of the world live in. One example has been filled in for you.

HOUSEBOAT

A NEW GIRL

CHAPTER EIGHT

The girls in this excerpt and book are in the fourth form, not fourth grade or class or standard. Fourth formers are 14 to 15-year-olds. In other words, they are in the 9th standard. How different they are from the teenagers of today!

Excerpt from *Claudine at St Clare's*

Before a week had gone by, a fourth new girl arrived. Mam'zelle herself announced her coming.

'I have a surprise for you,' she beamed one morning, coming in to give a French lesson. 'We shall soon have another companion in the fourth form. She arrives today.'

'Why is she so late in coming?' asked Pat, in surprise.

'She has just recovered from the measle,' said Mam'zelle, who always spoke of this illness in the singular and not in the plural. 'The measle is a most tiresome disease. Claudine had a very bad measle, and she could not come back any sooner.'

'Claudine?' said Isabel. 'What a pretty name! I like it.'

'Ah, and you will like the little Claudine too!' said Mam'zelle. 'For she is French. She is my niece!'

This was news to the girls. They hadn't even known that Mam'zelle had a niece. One coming to St Clare's too!

'I hope she will be happy at St Clare's,' said Hilary, feeling that someone ought to say the right thing.

'Ah, she will be very happy,' said Mam'zelle. 'She would be happy anywhere, the little Claudine. There never was such a child for happiness. Always she smiles and laughs, and always she plays the trick and the joke.'

This sounded good. The girls began to look forward to Claudine's coming. They looked at Mam'zelle expectantly, hoping to hear more.

Then Mam'zelle's face grew solemn. She pinched her glasses more firmly on her nose and gazed at the listening girls with her short-sighted, much-magnified eyes.

'I have especially asked for Claudine to come here,' she said. 'Before, she has been to a Convent School, but it was too strict for her, and always they found fault with the poor little Claudine. They said she cared nothing for anyone, nor for any rules or customs. And I thought to myself, "Ah, the good, hard-working Bobby was once like that-and see what St Clare's has done for her! Now she works for her Matric. and she is as good as gold! Maybe the same thing will happen to my little Claudine."'

Bobby looked uncomfortable as Mam'zelle made this speech. She wasn't at all sure that she wanted to be referred to as 'good as gold'. But Mam'zelle was so much in earnest that Bobby made no protest. It wouldn't have been any good, anyway! Mam'zelle swept on with her speech.

'And so the little Claudine comes today, well-recovered from the measle, and you will all give her a grand welcome, will you not? For your old Mam'zelle's sake?'

'Of course we'll make her welcome,' said Susan Howes, and most of the others murmured the same, except Angela, Alison and Pauline, who all put on a bored look, as if a niece belonging to Mam'zelle wasn't worth giving a thought to.

'Ah, you are good, kind girls,' said Mam'zelle. 'I will introduce Claudine to you as soon as she comes. She will love you all. She is a good girl though she seems to care nothing for what is good and proper. But you will change all that, *n'est-ce pas?*'

The girls thought that Claudine sounded distinctly amusing. It would be fun to have a French girl in the class! They glanced at one another, thinking that of all the new girls, this latest one sounded the most promising.

About five minutes before the lesson finished the door was opened, and a strange girl appeared. She was small, dark and smart. She had a very cheeky look and she gave a quick sidelong glance at the girls before advancing to Mam'zelle.

Mam'zelle gave a shriek, and then flung herself on the new girl. She kissed her several times on both cheeks, she stroked her dark hair, and poured out such a torrent of French that no one could follow it.

The girl replied in smooth, polite French, and kissed Mam'zelle on each cheek. She did not seem to mind her aunt's outburst in the least.

'Ah, *ma petite* Claudine, here you are at last!' cried Mam'zelle. She swung the girl round to face the class. 'Now see, here is the little Claudine,' said Mam'zelle, her glasses falling off her nose in her violent delight. 'Greet your new friends, Claudine.'

'Hallo, buddies!' said Claudine, amiably. The girls stared in surprise and then giggled. It was funny to hear such an American expression from the little French girl.

'What did you say?' said Mam'zelle, who was not well up in American slang. 'Did you say "hello, bodies"? That is not correct, Claudine. You should say, "Hallo, everybody."'

The class roared. Claudine grinned. Mam'zelle beamed. She was plainly very proud of Claudine and very fond of her.

COMPREHENSION CHECK!

Q What kind of a relationship do the girls have with Mam'zelle?

Q Why do the girls think Claudine might be fun to have around?

Q Why is Bobby uncomfortable with being referred to being as 'good as gold'?

Q Enid Blyton uses Mam'zelle's foreignness to create a comic effect. Write one reason why Mam'zelle makes you laugh.

How do you feel when someone new joins the class? Why do you feel that way?

Fill in the blanks by finding these lines in the excerpt you just read and writing the missing words.

a) The girls thought Claudine sounded ______________ amusing.

b) They looked at Mam'zelle ______________ hoping to hear more.

Now, use the missing words from the above lines and make two sentences.

1. ____

____

____

2. ____

____

____

Q **The class *roared.* Claudine *grinned*. Mam'zelle *beamed*. Enid Blyton uses three different verbs to convey the same emotion. Can you think of two verbs that convey the same emotion as *wept*?**

1. ____

2. ____

Q **Who said the following lines? Write the names in the space provided.**

a) 'Claudine? What a pretty name! I like it.'

____

b) 'Ah, she will be vary happy.'

____

c) 'Of course, we'll make her welcome.'

____

d) 'Hallo, buddies!'

____

What is the French word for the following English words?

ENGLISH	FRENCH
SCHOOL	
FRIEND	
TEACHER	
GIRL	
NIECE	

You are a student in the fourth form at St Clare's. Make a poster welcoming your new classmates to St Clare's.

THE WAILING VIOLIN

CHAPTER NINE

Excerpt from *Puzzle for the Secret Seven*

At first the three boys could not see the caravan at all, the night was so dark. They stumbled forward as quietly as they could, holding out their hands in front of them.

'Sh!' said Peter suddenly and stopped. The others bumped into him. 'Look!' whispered Peter. 'You can just see the outline of the caravan against the dark sky. Isn't that it?'

'Yes,' whispered back Colin. 'But there's no one there – it's quite dark.'

'Strange!' said Peter. 'Well – let's go as close as we can. Stop if you hear the slightest noise.'

They crept right up to the silent caravan. Not a chink of light was to be seen. Peter crept up the steps and listened. Ah –

there *was* a sound inside! But what was it?

'It's someone crying!' said Colin. Yes – there was someone sobbing quietly, like a child!

'It must be little Benny, left all alone in the van,' said Peter. 'Is the pram anywhere about?' He switched on his torch to see. But it was not in its usual place beside the caravan, and was nowhere to be seen. The sobbing still went on inside the van.

Then a voice made them jump almost out of their skins. It was old Matt again! He must have seen their torches and come over from his shack.

'Didn't I tell you lads to clear off home?' he said. 'Master Peter, does your father know you're out? And what are you doing on the steps of that caravan?'

'Matt – that wailing – it was someone playing a violin!' said Peter.

Matt stood silent a moment. Then he spoke in a voice of wonder. 'Young sir, you're right! But never did I hear a fiddle played like that afore. A-wailing and a-woe-ing! Who played it? There's no one in the Bolans' caravan, except young Benny tonight, that I do know for the Bolans asked me to keep an eye on it, while they went down to see someone about a cottage.'

'Oh – then it's poor little Benny crying in there because he's frightened of the wailing too!' said Peter. 'Shall we go in and comfort him?'

'No. He's afeard of people,' said the shepherd. 'But he's not afeard of old Matt! You let me see to him, Master Peter. I'll rock him to sleep like a weakly lamb! It's only that violin that's scared him. And that's a strange thing to be sure – someone up here making such mournful music at night!'

Matt walked into the dark caravan, making soft, comforting noises in his deep, kind voice. Peter flashed his torch swiftly inside, and saw Benny's dark head on a pillow in a corner. Old Matt bent over him.

The boys left the caravan in silence, and began to walk home. They were filled with curiosity and were extremely puzzled.

Peter spoke first. 'I don't understand all this. It *must* have been Luke playing that violin somewhere on the hillside. But why? Matt seems quite certain that he and Mrs Bolan went off to the town, and left Benny in the van. They took the baby with them, of course, as the pram is gone. Well, then – why did Luke Bolan apparently come back, all on his own, and play a violin?'

'I don't know,' said Colin. 'But I'm perfectly certain in my own mind that it was Luke who stole that violin, and uses it to comfort himself with because his banjo has been burnt. He may have left his wife down in the town for an hour or two, and come up here to play it.'

'Well – where do you suppose he hides it?' asked George. 'He must hide it jolly carefully somewhere – because if it were found he'd go to prison for theft!'

'He probably hides it in his caravan, under the mattress – or in the bread-bin, or some such place,' said Peter. 'I think we ought to come up tomorrow and see if we can find it. Luke will be off to some fair or other, earning his living, and we know Mrs Bolan takes the baby and Benny to go shopping. Janet and I met her in the town the other morning.'

'All right. We'll come up here tomorrow,' said George. 'I feel as if I MUST get to the bottom of this. It's all so strange – the fire – the missing scarecrow clothes – the stolen violin – the wailing in the night – and yet no one about to play the violin!'

'Look out!' hissed Colin suddenly, and the three stopped walking very suddenly. A figure stood not far off, still and silent in the big field. Peter chuckled.

'Ass! It's our old friend the scarecrow! I'm glad to see he's still wearing his new clothes. Come on – we shall all get into awful rows if we're much later!'

'What time shall we meet tomorrow?' asked George. 'Shall we all go – the whole

Secret Seven? We'll take something up to the Bolans as an excuse for calling.'

'Right. As near ten o'clock as you can manage,' said Peter. 'Then we can get back in good time for lunch.'

They parted at Peter's front gate and went to their homes, thinking over the night's adventure – for it really had been an adventure! All except that silly business when Susie and Binkie tried to upset everything!

I hope to goodness they don't get to hear that we're going up to the caravan tomorrow, thought George as he went home. Jack really ought to be more careful. He deserves to be chucked out of the Secret Seven if he can't keep Susie and her giggling friend in order!

Jack somehow managed to keep Susie in complete ignorance of what was happening, and arrived at Peter's in good time the next morning. Everyone was there. A very brief meeting was held, at which Peter explained to the girls and to Jack exactly what had happened the night before. They listened in astonishment and envy, especially poor old Jack, who had had to escort Susie and Binkie home!

'Gosh – to think it was someone playing a *violin*!' said Jack. 'I wish I'd heard it. Blow Susie! I bet it was Luke Bolan playing it! My word – what a bad lot he is – smashing a window to steal a really valuable old violin!'

'Come on,' said Peter, standing up. 'Yes, you too, Scamper. Mother's given us some butter and biscuits to take up to Mrs Bolan, so they will make a nice excuse for seeing her, if she happens to be there. If she isn't we shall have a chance to look inside the van to see if the violin is tucked away somewhere.'

Off they all went, Scamper running beside them, his tongue hanging out. Where were the Secret Seven off to now? Scamper didn't care if they were going to the moon, so long as he could go with them!

CROOKED CONNECTIONS!

The words in Column A need to find antonyms (from Column B) and synonyms (from Columns C). Draw lines between them and complete the connections. The first one has been done for you.

A	B	C
mournful	careless	quiet
ignorance	reached	sad
silent	ordinary	sobbing
carefully	joyful	innocence
arrived	laughing	curious
strange	noisy	watchfully
crying	knowledge	departed

WHO SAYS THESE LINES?

a) 'I don't understand all this. It must have been Luke playing that violin somewhere on the hillside. But why? Matt seems quite certain that he and Mrs Bolan went off to the town, and left Benny in the van. They took the baby with them, of course, as the pram is gone. Well, then – why did Luke Bolan apparently come back, all on his own, and play a violin?'

____

b) 'Gosh – to think it was someone playing a violin! I wish I'd heard it. Blow Susie! I bet it was Luke Bolan playing it! My word – what a bad lot he is – smashing a window to steal a really valuable old violin!'

____

c) 'What time shall we meet tomorrow?' asked ______________. 'Shall we all go – the whole Secret Seven? We'll take something up to the Bolans as an excuse for calling.'

____

d) 'It must be little Benny, left all alone in the van. Is the pram anywhere about?'

____

Fill in the blanks by reading the excerpt.

a. The young sleuths think they hear Luke playing a stolen violin. Luke's own ______________ has been burnt.

b. The boys go snooping around a caravan. They notice a baby's 'vehicle' missing. That would be a ______________.

c. The Bolans live in a caravan. But Matt lives in a ______________.

d. The sounds of the violin appear to have come from the hillside. But Matt believes the couple has gone into ______________.

Use these words from the excerpt to make simple two-line rhymes. The first one has been done for you.

a. **Bread-bin**

A bread-bin is a tin

to keep bread in!

b. **Stumble**

____

____

c. **Fiddle**

____

____

A RIDING ACCIDENT

CHAPTER TEN

Excerpt from *Malory Towers: Summer Term* by Pamela Cox

The others had noticed that the two girls looked unusually serious too, and glanced at one another apprehensively, as Felicity asked in alarm, 'I say, what's up? Don't tell me there has been more trouble over at Five Oaks?'

'I'm afraid that there has,' said Julie, her open, freckled face looking troubled. 'Someone has been hurt.'

'No!' gasped Susan. 'Who?'

'Let's go and sit under that tree,' said Julie, as a noisy group of first formers began playing with a ball nearby. 'And we'll tell you all about it.'

So the third formers sat in the shade of a large apple tree

and Lucy said, 'Bill was riding Thunder and showing a group of children how to take one of the practice jumps, when she fell off. We don't know how badly hurt she is yet, but it looks as if she's injured her arm.'

'*Bill?*' repeated June, incredulously. 'But Bill is a superb horsewoman! How could she possibly have had an accident taking one of those titchy little jumps?'

'That's just it,' said Julie, lowering her voice. 'It was no accident!'

'Whatever do you mean,' asked Freddie, looking puzzled.

'Well,' began Julie, 'when Bill fell off, everyone ran across to help her, of course. Miss Peters was there – she's great friends with Bill and Clarissa, you know – and she said it looked as if the reins had snapped. But a little later, once all the fuss had died down, Lucy and I took a look at the reins, and it was quite clear that the reins hadn't snapped – they had been cut.'

'That's right,' said Lucy. 'It was a clean, straight cut, and there was no sign of wear, or fraying, as there would have been if they had simply snapped. Whoever did it only cut part of the way through, so that Bill wouldn't notice it immediately.'

'But why didn't Miss Peters notice that they had been cut?' asked Freddie, looking puzzled.

'She was more concerned with Bill than anything else,'

said Julie. 'And she only glanced quickly at the reins.'

'So where is Bill now?' asked Felicity.

'At the hospital,' answered Lucy. 'Mr Banks took her there in his car and Miss Peters went with them.'

'Mr Banks? What on earth was he doing there?' asked Susan, astonished.

'Oh, he wasn't there, but Eleanor was,' said Julie. 'She saw at once that we needed someone with a car to take Bill to hospital, so she telephoned him from Five Oaks and he was there in a trice. I must say that he's quite different from what I expected.'

'Yes, he seemed awfully nice,' put in Lucy. 'And he was so concerned about Bill. He said that he would wait at the hospital for her and Miss Peters, and bring them both home again.'

'Quite different from Eleanor, then,' said June dryly. 'I say, Julie, who else was over at Five Oaks?'

Julie wrinkled her brow thoughtfully and said, 'A few youngsters from the village – oh, and Patsy and Rose from the second form. They have just started taking riding lessons. Then, of course, there was Jim, the stable boy.'

YOU DON'T *SAY*... AT LEAST NOT ALWAYS!

Read this excerpt carefully. Notice the italicized, underlined word *said* that occurs a few times in the conversation between the girls. The words in bold are other verbs that may mean the same as *said*, but that also tell us something more about the way the character reacts. For instance, **gasped** tells us that Susan is shocked to hear Julie's news. In the same way, when Julie **lowers her voice**, we know that she wants to keep her suspicions secret.

The others had noticed that the two girls looked unusually serious too, and glanced at one another apprehensively, as Felicity **asked in alarm**, 'I say, what's up? Don't tell me there has been more trouble over at Five Oaks?'

'I'm afraid that there has,' *said* Julie, her open, freckled face looking troubled. 'Someone has been hurt.'

'No!' **gasped** Susan. 'Who?'

'Let's go and sit under that tree,' *said* Julie, as a noisy group of first formers began playing with a ball nearby. 'And we'll tell you all about it.'

So the third formers sat in the shade of a large apple tree and Lucy *said*, 'Bill was riding Thunder, and showing a group of children how to take one of the practice jumps, when she fell off. We don't know how badly hurt she is yet, but it looks as if she's injured her arm.'

'*Bill*?' **repeated June, incredulously**. 'But Bill is a superb horsewoman! How could she possibly have had an accident taking one of those titchy little jumps?'

'That's just it,' *said* **Julie, lowering her voice**. 'It was no accident!'

'Whatever do you mean,' **asked Freddie, looking puzzled**.

'Well,' **began** Julie, 'when Bill fell off, everyone ran across to help her, of course. Miss Peters was there – she's great friends with Bill and Clarissa, you know – and she said it looked as if the reins had snapped. But a little later, once all the fuss had died down, Lucy and I took a look at the reins, and it was quite clear that the reins hadn't snapped – they had been cut.'

'That's right,' *said* Lucy. 'It was a clean, straight cut, and there was no sign of wear, or fraying, as there would have been if they had simply snapped. Whoever did it only cut part of the way through, so that Bill wouldn't notice it immediately.'

Now write your own dialogue of 6–8 lines between Julie and Lucy in which they discuss how they can make Bill feel better after the accident. Use words other than 'said' to describe the characters' reactions to one another.

WHO ARE THEY?

Identify who these characters are – that is, if they are students, teachers or others – and write the answers alongside. One has been done for you.

Julie	Third-form student
Jim	
Patsy and Rose	
Thunder	
Bill	
Miss Peters	

A JOB FOR TIMMY

CHAPTER ELEVEN

Excerpt from *Five Go Down to the Sea*

Julian paused on the last step of the spiral staircase and listened. Not a sound came from the nearby room.

'Who's there?' said Julian, sharply. 'I know you're there! I heard you!'

Still not a sound! The kitchen, overgrown with weeds and dark with ivy and the white rambling rose, seemed to be listening to him, but there was no answer!

Julian stepped right into the room and looked round. Nothing was there – nobody was there! The place was absolutely empty and quiet. Julian went through a doorway into another room. That was empty too. The old house only had four rooms altogether, two of them very tiny, and every one of them was empty. Timmy didn't seem disturbed at all, either, nor did he bark as he certainly would have done if there had been any intruder there.

'Well, Timmy, it's a false alarm,' said Julian, relieved. 'Must have been a rabbit, or even a bit of wall crumbling and falling. What are you sniffing at there?'

Timmy was sniffing with interest at a corner near the doorway. He stood and looked at Julian as if he would like to tell him something. Julian went over to see what it was.

There was nothing there except for some rather flattened weeds, growing through the floor. Julian couldn't think why Timmy should be interested. However, Timmy soon wandered away and went all round the place, wondering why they had come to such a peculiar house.

'Dick! Bring the girls down!' shouted Julian up the stone stairway. 'There doesn't seem to be anyone here, after all. It must have been some small animal that Anne heard.'

The others clattered down in relief. 'I'm sorry I gave you all a shock,' said Anne. 'But it did sound like somebody down there! However, I'm sure Timmy would have barked if so! He didn't seem at all disturbed.'

'No. I think we can safely say that it was a false alarm,' said Dick. 'What do we do next? Have our lunch? Or hunt about to see if we can find the entrance to the passage that leads from here down to the coves?'

Julian looked at his watch. 'It's not really time for lunch yet, unless you're all frightfully hungry,' he said.

'Well, I'm beginning to feel jolly hungry,' said Dick. 'But, on the other hand, I feel I can't wait to find that passage! Where on earth is the entrance?'

'I've been in all four rooms,' said Julian. 'None of them

seems to have anything but weeds in, no old door leading out of the walls, no trapdoor. It's a puzzle.'

'Well, we'll all have a jolly good hunt,' said George. 'This is the sort of thing I like. Timmy, you hunt too!'

They began to explore the four rooms of the old house. As weeds grew more or less all over the floor they felt that there could be no trapdoor. If there had been, and the man with the lamp used it, the weeds would surely have shown signs of it. But they grew quite undisturbed.

'Listen,' said Julian at last. 'I've got an idea. We'll make Timmy find the entrance.'

'How?' said George at once.

'Well, we'll make him smell the oil drips on the steps, and follow with his nose any others that have dripped in the weeds,' said Julian. 'I don't suppose the lamp dripped only on the steps. It must have dripped all the way from the passage entrance, wherever it is, to the top of the tower. Couldn't Timmy sniff them out? They would lead us to the entrance we're trying to find!'

'All right. But I'm beginning to believe there is no entrance,' said George, getting hold of Timmy's collar. 'We've looked over every single inch of this house. Come on, Tim, you've got to perform a miracle!'

Timmy's nose was firmly placed over the oil-drip on the bottom stair.

'Sniff it, Timmy, and follow,' said George.

Timmy knew perfectly well what she meant. George had trained him well! He sniffed hard at the oil and then started up the stone steps for the next oil patch. But George pulled him back.

'No, Tim. Not that way. This way. There must be other oil drips on the floor of the house.'

Timmy amiably turned the other way. He found an oil drip at once, on a patch of weeds growing on the floor. He sniffed it and went on to another and another.

'Good old Timmy,' said George, delighted. 'Isn't he clever, Ju? He's following where the man walked when he carried that lamp! Go on, Timmy, where's the next drip?'

It was an easy, strong-smelling trail for Timmy to follow! He followed it, sniffing, out of one room into another, smaller one. Then into a third, bigger one, which must have been the main room, for it had a very big fireplace. Timmy went straight to the fireplace, his nose to the ground. In fact, he went right into the hearth, and there came to a stop. He looked round at George and barked.

'He says the trail ends here,' said George, in excitement. 'So the entrance to the secret passage must be in this big fireplace!'

The others crowded to the hearth. Julian produced his torch and shone it up the chimney. It was an enormous one, though part of the top of it had now fallen away.

'Nothing there,' said Julian. 'But – hallo – what's this?'

COMPREHENSION CHECK!

Q Describe the old house mentioned in the excerpt in your own words.

Q What smell does Timmy follow to get to the entrance to the secret passage?

Q At the beginning of the excerpt, why does Julian come into the house on his own?

Q There appears to be thriving vegetation in the old house. What are the plants mentioned in the excerpt?

Q Have you ever been inside an old house? They can sometimes make noises. Give five reasons why old houses might creak and groan.

Fill in the blanks based on the excerpt you just read.

a) Julian thinks that the sound Anne heard was ______________________
____.

b) Timmy wonders why he has come to ______________________
____.

c) Julian finds the house to be ______________________
____.

d) George thinks the entrance to the passage must be ______________
____.

e) George thinks Timmy is following the man where ______________
____.

In the excerpt Timmy finds oil stains that lead him to a chimney. Pretend you are with the Five, and in the space given below write down three other clues that you might find in the old house. Based on your clues, take a guess at what kind of person might be using the place.

CLUES	DEDUCTION
1.	
2.	
3.	

LUKE WHO'S TALKING!

CHAPTER TWELVE

Excerpt from *The Mystery of the Disappearing Cat*

The five children sat on top of the wall, with Buster scratching at the bricks below. They wondered what to do. Pip looked at his watch.

'Just gone quarter to six,' he said. 'Can Luke have gone home? No; he surely would have spoken to us first.'

'Perhaps old Clear-Orf is questioning him,' said Fatty. This seemed very likely. The children wished they could find out.

Fatty had a good idea. 'Look here, Pip,' he said, 'you could find out what's happening if you liked.'

'How?' asked Pip.

'Well, your mother has just

been to tea next door, hasn't she,' said Fatty.

'You could hop over the wall, and go and see what's happening; and if anyone sees you and wants to know what you are doing there, you could say your mother has just been to tea, and has she by any chance dropped her hanky in the garden?'

'But she hasn't,' said Pip. 'Didn't you see her take it out of her bag when she was talking to us? It had a most lovely smell.'

'Of course I did, idiot,' said Fatty impatiently. 'It's only just an excuse.

'You don't need to say she did drop her hanky, because we know she didn't – but you could easily say, "Had she?" couldn't you?'

'It's a good idea of Fatty's,' said Larry. 'It's about the only way any of us could get into the garden without being sent out at once by Clear-Orf or Tupping. Go on, Pip. Jump down and see whether you can find out what's happening. Hurry up. It's really a great bit of luck that your mother has just been there to tea.'

Pip was anxious to go – and yet very much afraid of meeting Tupping or Clear-Orf. He jumped down, waved to the others, and set off through the bushes.

There was no sign of Luke at all. Pip passed by the cat-house, but there was no one there either. He peeped into the cage where Dark Queen should have been with the others. The cats looked at him and mewed. Pip went on down the path, round by the greenhouses, and then stood hidden in the bushes. He could hear voices nearby.

He peeped through the bushes. There was a little group of people on the lawn.

Pip knew most of them.

'There's Lady Candling,' he thought. 'And that's Miss Tremble – doesn't she look upset! And there's Tupping, looking very pleased and important – and that's old Clear-Orf, the bobby! And oh, there's poor old Luke!'

Poor Luke was there, in the centre, looking quite bewildered and terribly scared. The policeman was standing opposite to him, big black notebook in hand, and Luke was stammering and stuttering out replies to questions that Mr Goon was barking out at him.

At the back were two maids, plainly the cook and the parlourmaid, both looking excited. They were whispering together, nudging one another.

Pip crept nearer. He could hear the questions now that were fired at poor frightened Luke.

'What were you doing all the afternoon?'

'I was – I was – digging up the old peas – in the Long Bed,' stammered Luke.

'Is that the bed by the cat-house?' asked Mr Goon, scribbling something down in his book.

'Y-y-y-yes, sir,' stuttered Luke.

'So you were by the cats the whole afternoon?' said the policeman. 'Did anyone come near them?'

'Miss T-t-tremble came at f-f-four o'clock about, with another l-l-lady,' said Luke, pushing back his untidy hair. 'They stayed a few minutes and went.'

'And what did you do between four and five o'clock?' said Mr Goon in a very threatening sort of voice.

Luke looked as if he was going to fall down in terror. 'N-n-nothing, sir – only d-d-d-dug!' he stammered. 'Just d-d-d dug – alongside the cat-house. And nobody came near, not a soul, till you and Mr Tupping came along to see the cats.'

'And we found that Dark Queen was gone,' said Mr Tupping in a fierce voice.

'Well, Mr Goon – the evidence is as plain as plain, isn't it? He took that cat – no doubt about it – and handed her to some friend of his for a bit of pocket money. He's a bad boy is Luke, and always has been ever since I had him.'

'I'm not bad, Mr Tupping!' shouted Luke, suddenly finding a little courage. 'I've never took a thing I shouldn't! I've worked hard for you! I've stood things from you I shouldn't stand. You know I'd never steal one of them cats. I'd be too scared to, even if I thought of it!'

'That's enough, now, that's enough,' said Mr Goon fiercely. 'Don't you go talking to Mr Tupping like that. What boys like you want is a good hiding.'

'Ah, I'll see he gets it all right,' said Mr Tupping in a horrid voice. 'I'll have a word with his stepfather. He knows what this lad's like, right enough.'

'I think, Tupping,' said Lady Candling in her low, clear voice, 'I think there is no need to say anything to Luke's stepfather until we know a little more about this curious happening.'

Tupping looked rather taken aback. He had been enjoying himself so much that he had half-forgotten Lady Candling was there. Luke turned to his mistress.

'Please, Mam,' he said in an urgent voice, 'please, Mam, I do beg of you not to believe what Mr Tupping and Mr Goon say about me. I didn't take Dark Queen. I don't know where she is. I've never taken a thing I shouldn't take from your garden!'

'And that's a lie!' said Mr Tupping in a triumphant voice. 'What about them strawberry runners?'

To Pip's horror, poor Luke, now frightened and upset beyond bearing, burst into enormous sobs that shook his big body in an alarming manner. He put his arm across his face, trying to hide it.

'Let him go home,' said Lady Candling in a gentle voice. 'You have questioned him enough. He's only a fifteen-year-old boy, after all. Mr Goon, I ask you to go now, please, and Luke, you may go home too.'

COMPREHENSION CHECK!

Who is old Clear-Orf?

Who is Dark Queen?

Who is Mr Tupping?

Who is Luke?

Based on the excerpt, what do you know about:

a) Mr Tupping

b) Lady Candling

SLEUTH ALERT!

Part of being a good detective is being able to read people well. This includes not only what they say but also their mannerisms and behaviour. Let us examine the evidence from what Luke told Mr Goon and Mr Tupping.

Q Luke stammers when he speaks to Mr Goon. Do you think that proves his guilt? Why or why not?

Q Who do you think the other lady who came with Miss Tremble is?

Q Do you think Luke took the strawberry runners from Lady Candling's garden? Give reasons for your answer.

CATCALL!

Write down ten words that start with 'cat'. For example, category, catastrophe, etc.

A QUARREL, AND A PICNIC!

CHAPTER THIRTEEN

Excerpt from *Five Have a Mystery to Solve*

Timmy was waiting for the children at the top of the hill, his tail waving, his mouth open as he panted. He picked something up as the children came, threw it into the air and caught it.

'Another golf ball, Timmy?' said Dick, as Timmy threw the ball into the air again with a toss of his big head.

'No – it's too big for that,' said George. 'Drop it, Timmy. What have you found?'

Timmy dropped the ball at George's feet. It was bigger than a golf ball and had a hole right through it.

'Oh, it's one of those balls that children throw up and

try to catch on a stick,' said George. 'Somebody must have dropped it. All right, Tim, you can have it.'

'He won't swallow it, will he?' said Wilfrid anxiously. 'It's not *very* big – and I once saw a dog swallow something by mistake, that he threw into the air to catch.'

'Timmy is *much* too sensible to swallow *any* ball,' said George. 'You needn't worry about *him*. Anyway, *I* can do any worrying necessary. He's *my* dog.'

'All right, all right, all right!' said Wilfrid. 'Miss High-and-Mighty can look after her own dog. Fine!'

George looked round at him furiously and he made a face at her. Then he whistled to Timmy – yes, he actually dared to whistle to him!

'Nobody whistles for my dog except me,' said George. 'And anyway, he won't come to *you*.'

But, to her surprise and horror, Timmy *did* go to Wilfrid, and pranced all around him, expecting a game. George called him sternly, and he looked at her in surprise. He began to trot over to her when Wilfred whistled again, and obediently Timmy turned as if to go to him.

George caught hold of the dog's collar, and aimed a punch at the whistling boy. It missed him, and he danced around, laughing.

'Stop it now, you two,' said Julian, seeing George's look of fury. 'I said STOP IT! Wilfrid, go on ahead, and *keep* going. George, don't be an idiot. He's only teasing you to make you lose your temper. Don't please him by losing it!'

George said nothing more but her eyes blazed.

'Oh dear,' thought Anne, 'now we won't have any peace! She won't forgive Wilfrid for making Timmy go to him! Wilfrid really is a pain sometimes.'

They were all very hungry for their lunch and very pleased with everything that Anne provided. Dick went into the little cottage to help her.

George insisted on keeping her hand on Timmy's collar all the time, in case Wilfrid should entice him to his side.

'He's making some of his strange noises now,' said Dick to Anne. 'Noises that animals can't seem to resist! I'm not surprised that George has got Timmy tightly by the collar! I'm not a dog but I find those little whiny noises Wilfrid is making very strange indeed, and I'd love to go nearer!'

'Well, I hope we're not going to have black looks from George from now on,' said Anne. 'Wilfrid's an idiot at times, and VERY irritating but he's not bad underneath, if you know what I mean.'

'Well, I don't really,' said Dick, cutting some tomatoes in half. 'I think he's a badly brought-up little pain – and if I were a dog, I'd bite him, not fawn on him! Have I cut up enough tomatoes, Anne?'

'Good gracious, yes!' said Anne. 'However many do you think we're going to eat – forty or fifty? Look, you open this tin for me, Dick. I do so hate opening tins. I nearly always cut myself.'

'Don't you ever open one again, then,' said Dick. 'I'm the official tin-opener from now on! Dear old Anne, whatever should we do without you! You take everything on your shoulders, and we just let you! George ought to help more. She's a girl like you – but she never gets the meals or anything. I'll tick her off one of these days.'

'No, don't,' said Anne, in alarm. 'I like doing things on my own. George would only break things or upset them. She's as ham-handed as a boy when it comes to washing up or setting out crockery, though she means well.'

'So boys are ham-handed, are they?' said Dick, pretending to be offended. 'When have I ever broken anything, I'd like to know? I'm as careful as any girl, when I handle crockery!'

Alas for Dick! The glass he was holding suddenly slipped from his hand, fell to the floor, and broke! Anne looked at him and gave a sudden delighted giggle.

'Old Ham-hand!' she said. 'Can't pick up a glass without dropping it! Look, take out this tray for me, and for goodness sake, don't drop that!'

They all had a delicious lunch, and ate practically everything. Wilfrid sat a little away from everyone, scattering crumbs around as he ate. Birds of all kinds were soon round him, even hopping on to his hands. A magpie flew down to his left shoulder. Wilfrid greeted it like an old friend. 'Hallo, Maggie Pie! How's the family? I hope Polly Pie has recovered from her cold. And is Peter Pie's bad leg better? And what about old Grandpa Pie – does he still chase you young ones?'

The magpie put its glossy head on one side and chattered back to him in bird-language, which Wilfrid appeared to understand. He stroked the bird's gleaming breast, and fondled it lovingly. George deliberately didn't watch. She turned her back on Wilfrid and the magpie, and talked to Timmy.

The others couldn't help being amused. The magpie put Wilfrid's conversation to an end very suddenly. The boy was about to put half a tomato into his mouth when the bird bent down its head and snatched away the tomato with its powerful beak. Then it rose quickly into the air on its big wings, making a noise exactly as if it were laughing!

Everyone roared with laughter except the surprised Wilfrid. 'He's gone to take your tomato to Polly Pie, I should think,' said Anne, and that made everyone laugh again.

'I'll have another tomato now, please,' said Wilfrid.

'Sorry. You're unlucky. They're all gone,' said Dick.

It was lovely sitting up on the hillside, watching the boats in the harbour, and seeing the beautiful, white-sailed yachts bending to and fro in the strong wind that blew there. They could all see Whispering Island quite clearly, and noticed that no boats went anywhere near it. Clearly everyone knew that men might be there, watching for intruders.

WHAT COMES FIRST

Our memory is scrambled and we've forgotten the sequence of events! Help us by writing out the sentences in the right order.

1. *Anne and Dick get lunch ready.*
2. *George and Wilfrid have an argument.*
3. *Dick thinks Wilfrid is badly brought up.*
4. *Everyone notices that boats don't seem to go anywhere near Whispering Island.*
5. *Julian breaks up the quarrel between George and Wilfrid.*
6. *A magpie steals Wilfrid's tomato and flies away.*
7. *Timothy finds a ball to play with.*
8. *Dick breaks a glass.*

GENDER ROLES

As you can see from this excerpt, Enid Blyton wrote at a time when the roles played by boys and girls at home and outside were different from what they are now. Give two examples from the excerpt where you see girls/boys play old-fashioned roles. For example, *'George ought to help more. She's a girl like you – but she never gets the meals or anything. I'll tick her off one of these days.'*

1. ______________________________

____

____

____

____

____

2. ______________________________

____

____

____

____

____

SHARP-EYED SLEUTH!

We have changed the following sentences by modifying words/phrases from the original text. Spot the difference and write the correct answer in the space provided.

1. George grabbed the dog's collar, and aimed a punch at the whistling boy.

2. George looked round at him angrily and he made a face at her.

3. You take on all the responsibility and we just let you!

4. The magpie put its shiny head on one side and chattered back to him in bird-language.

5. It was lovely sitting up on the hillside, watching the boats in the harbour, and seeing the beautiful, white-sailed yachts bending this way and that way in the strong wind that blew there.

The excerpt begins on a note of mild disharmony and irritation, but the mood becomes ominous in the end. What sentence introduces a sense of danger to the scene?

SPOT THE DIFFERENCES

Spot 5 differences between the two pictures and circle them.

CHAPTER FOURTEEN

EVERYONE'S ANGRY WITH PRUDENCE

Excerpt from *Summer Term at St Clare's*

Carlotta was a very popular person after this upheaval. Her complete honesty and frankness had disarmed everyone, and to most of the girls she suddenly appeared as a most surprising and romantic person. Even the second-formers were thrilled, though as a rule they professed rather to turn up their noses at anything that happened in the first form. But Tessie, Queenie, and the rest of the second form were just as persistent as the lower form in begging Carlotta to show off her circus tricks and accomplishments.

'It must have been a bit of a shock to that sneak of a Prudence to find that instead of looking down on our Carlotta we looked up to her and admired her instead!' said Pat. 'I bet dear darling Prudence thought we'd be shocked to the back teeth to hear she was a circus-girl. I vote we punish her by not taking a scrap of notice of her, and not listening to anything she says!'

'I think we ought to do the same to Pam then,' said Bobby. 'Pam's Prudence's friend, you know, and she was with her when they spied on Carlotta. She's a silly little creature and thinks the world of Prudence. It will do her good to feel that we don't approve of Prudence's ways, and don't particularly want to be pleasant to Prudence's friends.'

'Well, I'm rather sorry for Pam,' said Isabel. 'She's a nervous little thing and awfully hard-working. Don't let's be too hard on her.'

Prudence didn't at all like the treatment meted out to her by the first-formers. The girl was very fond of the sound of her own voice, and it was most annoying to her to find that whenever she began to air her views about anything, all the girls around either suddenly disappeared, or else began to talk nonsense to one another at the tops of their voices.

Prudence would perhaps address herself to Hilary and say 'Hilary, what side are you taking in tonight's debate on "Should women rule the world?" I'm taking the side that they certainly should. After all, don't we...'

Then Hilary would suddenly address Janet in a very loud voice and say something perfectly ridiculous, such as 'I say, Janet, old thing, how many legs has a kitten?' And Janet, perfectly solemn, would answer in a loud voice 'Well, usually four. But you'd better count and see.'

Prudence would stare in astonishment, and then begin again. 'What I say is, if women ruled the world...'

Then Kathleen would chime in, cutting right across Prudence's rather affected little voice. 'Hilary, Janet! Do you suppose a worm really grows into two worms when it's cut in half?'

Then Bobby would cut in, rather cruelly. 'What about cutting dear Prudence in two, then we'll see!'

And so it went on, nobody ever paying any attention to Prudence at all. Prudence was hurt and angry and went to Pam for comfort. She squeezed out a few tears and Pam tried to comfort her.

'Pam, you know quite well I wasn't spying on Carlotta,' wept Prudence. 'Can't you tell the girls I wasn't? Do stick up for me. What's the good of being my friend if you don't?'

And then poor Pam, trying her hardest to be loyal, would stick up for Prudence,

although in her heart of hearts she no longer really trusted or liked her. But the thirteen-year-old girl was easily swayed, and anyone in tears moved her heart.

So it came about that very soon the first-formers began to ignore poor Pam too, and laughed at her efforts to stick up for Prudence. Pam retired into her shell and felt very unhappy. She worried about the whole thing and turned to her work more than ever to help her to forget the many unpleasantnesses that seemed to be cropping up in those weeks.

Now that her secret was out, Carlotta was very happy. Hers was an honest nature, and she had not liked keeping everything to herself. Now the whole school knew what she was and eyed her with wonder, half-expecting her to do something extraordinary at any time. The twins took her under their wing, and they and Carlotta, Bobby and Janet were continually about together.

Carlotta had gone to Miss Theobald and had told her that everyone now knew she had once been a circus-girl. 'But they don't seem to mind,' said Carlotta, looking straight at the Head Mistress with her fearless eyes. 'You thought they would, didn't you?'

'No, Carlotta, I didn't think that most of them would mind at all,' said Miss Theobald. 'But I thought it might be easier for you to settle down if the girls did not regard you as anything out of the ordinary. Also your father begged me to keep your "secret" as he called it. Well – it's out now – and you must just show me that it doesn't matter. You are all your father has, you know – so try and get used to the kind of life you will have to lead with him later on.'

Carlotta sighed. She didn't want to lead any other kind of life except the one she had always known – the life of the circus-camp, always on the move, always visiting new places, always making new friends. She left Miss Theobald's drawing-room looking rather subdued.

After a while the excitement caused by the row in Mam'zelle's class, and by Carlotta's secret died down a little. This was partly because matches were looming ahead – tennis and swimming – and the school was putting in a good deal of practice, hoping to win all the matches against other schools.

The twins were practising hard, and Bobby was helping them. Don't-Care Bobby would not do anything much to help herself on, but never minded how much time she gave to help anyone else to become better at anything. Janet and Hilary were both practising too, but were not so good as the twins.

'You're getting a grand style at tennis, both of you,' said Belinda Towers, approvingly, as she watched the twins one afternoon. 'If you go on like this you'll be chosen for the first form team against St Christopher's! Bobby, you're getting better too. Why don't you try a bit harder and see if you can't be the reserve girl?'

Two out of each form were chosen to play against two girls from each form of the opposing school, and for each two there was a reserve girl, in case one of the two fell ill or could not play for any other reason. Bobby shook her head when she heard Belinda say this.

'No, thanks!' she said. 'It makes tennis too much like hard work if I have to practise up for reserve girl!'

Belinda was not amused by this answer. She gave Bobby a look that rather surprised her, because it held a certain amount of scorn in it. 'Oh, well,' said Belinda, 'of course we can't expect Don't-Care Bobby to care enough for the school, or to have enough pride in her form to do anything that might seem like hard work. Foolish of me to suggest it!'

COMPREHENSION CHECK!

Q What is Carlotta's big secret?

Q How do the girls treat Prudence in this excerpt? Do you feel sorry for her? Why or why not?

Q Does Pam do the right thing by trying to support Prudence? Give two reasons for your answer.

Find a sentence from the text to show that:

1. Belinda is upset with Bobby.

2. Carlotta is relieved.

3. Bobby has a helpful nature.

4. Bobby can also be mean.

5. Everyone is mad at Prudence.

Q What do the following phrases mean? Look up a dictionary if you aren't sure!

1. Under their wing

2. Out of the ordinary

3. Turn up their noses

Make sentences with the following words:

DISARM

PROFESS

PERSISTENT

ACCOMPLISHMENT

RIDICULOUS

UPHEAVAL

Sum up the excerpt you just read in ten sentences. The first line of the summary has been done for you.

Carlotta becomes very popular after everyone discovers her secret.

Enid Blyton

SHOWTIME

There's one word hidden in this tent. Find it.

P	Q	R	S	T	X	Y	Z	P	Q	R
Q	R	S	T	X	Y	Z	C	C	C	C
R	S	T	X	Y	Z	P	Q	R	S	T
S	T	X	Y	C	P	Q	R	S	T	X
T	P	Q	R	I	Q	T	S	T	X	Y
X	Y	R	S	R	X	Y	Z	P	Q	Z
Y	Z	S	T	C	Y	Z	P	Q	R	S
Z	P	T	X	U	Z	P	Q	R	S	T
P	Q	X	Y	S	P	X	Y	Z	P	Q
Q	R	Y	Z	P	Q	R	S	T	X	Y
R	S	Z	P	Q	R	S	T	X	Y	Z

WHO'S THE GUY?

CHAPTER FIFTEEN

Excerpt from *Secret Seven Fireworks*

'Go on – do read it,' said Janet impatiently.

'*It is reported this afternoon that two of the thieves who robbed Mrs Strangeway's house on Monday night have been caught by the police. They had not left the district. The third man ran away and escaped. The police have a full description of him. He is stout, tall, and has a moustache and red hair. Unfortunately the stolen articles have not yet been recovered. Anyone having seen a man of the above description is asked to contact the police.*'

'Gosh!' said Peter as Colin finished reading. 'So they've got two of the men already. What a pity the other man escaped.'

'Yes – and took the stuff with him, I suppose,' said Colin gloomily. 'My poor old granny is in an awful state as you can imagine. She had to go to bed with shock as soon as she got back, and my mother sent for the doctor. If only she could get back the things she prized most – my grandfather's silver cups – the ones he won for all kinds of sport – and the jewellery that's been in her family for years. I wish the police had got the stolen stuff instead of the robbers!'

'Probably the two thieves who were caught will soon confess where they hid it,' said Pam.

'Well, I should think the third man, who wasn't caught, will certainly go and take the things from whatever hiding place they are in now, and hide them somewhere else!' said Peter. 'Just in case his pals gave away the hiding place! He could then just wait a bit till all the hue and cry has died down, and take them for himself!'

'Yes, I suppose he could,' said Colin, laying down the paper. 'Fancy the men still being in the district. You'd have thought they would have got away as soon as possible.'

'I bet the man who's free will have put a hundred miles between himself and the police by now,' said Jack.

'If he hasn't, he'll find it difficult to move about in the daytime,' said Colin. 'You can shave off your moustache but you can't hide your fatness – or your ginger hair!'

'You *can* hide your hair – dye it, say – or wear a hat, silly,' said Barbara.

'Let's get on with the guy,' said Janet. 'What do you think of him, Colin?'

She and Pam pulled the guy in front of Colin. He looked very strange in his big trousers, carefully safety-pinned in place, his enormous dirty old tweed coat, and large rubber boots. Scamper began to bark angrily, again.

'He simply can't bear our guy,' said Pam. 'Did you get a mask, Colin? Oh yes, there it is. Put it on the guy, then we can put the cap on his head.'

Colin carefully fitted the big mask over the front of the guy's head. Everyone roared with laughter. The guy seemed very real now he had a face!

'Isn't it odd – you've chosen a mask with a red moustache!' said Janet. 'Like the robber who got away! Mr Guy Fawkes, are you sure you're not the third robber?'

The guy stared solemnly at her, and Scamper growled again. He really did not like the guy at all.

'Take the mask off and squeeze the head a bit to make the mask fit better,' said George. 'It sticks out over his chest too much.'

'They took off the mask, and pummelled the head till it was a better shape. Then on went the mask again, and Scamper gave another volley of angry barks.

'Now the cap,' said George and solemnly placed it on the guy's head, screwing it round a bit to give it a jaunty, rakish look. The Seven laughed uproariously. The guy looked really comical with his cap on.

'How do you do, Mr Fawkes?' said George, and shook him by the hand. 'I hope you are feeling well and looking forward to warming yourself on our bonfire next week.'

'He looks awfully uncomfortable sitting on that box.' said Janet. 'And he's heavy to hold up straight. Can't we get him an old chair, or something, to sit in? He'll last a lot longer on top of the bonfire if he's sitting up.'

'I think there's an old chair, with arms, in the stables,' said Peter. 'Nobody uses it now. Let's go and get it, shall we?' They all trooped out of the shed, Scamper too, leaving the guy sprawled over his box.

COMPREHENSION CHECK!

Q Who is Mrs Strangeway?

Q The children keep talking about 'the guy', but they also talk about Guy Fawkes. The latter was a member of a group that planned to assassinate King James I of England in 1605. Who is 'the guy' that the children keep referring to?

Q What do they plan to do with the guy?

Q Why do you think Scamper doesn't like the guy?

____

____

____

____

TRY ANOTHER ONE

Q Pummel means to beat up badly. Can you think of two other words for pummel?

______________________,

____

Q Can you think of two other words for awful?

______________________,

____

Q Can you think of two other words for solemn?

______________________,

____

WHAT'S THAT WORD AGAIN?!

Choose the right word and fill in the blanks.

1. Colin's grandmother is ______________________ to find she's been robbed.
   a) demented
   b) delighted
   c) dismayed
2. Colin thinks it is ______________________ that one of the thieves escaped.
   a) unlikely
   b) unbearable
   c) unfortunate
3. The guy looks very ______________________ in his big trousers.
   a) peculiar
   b) princely
   c) possible
4. The cap gives the guy a rather ______________________ look.
   a) jumpy
   b) jolly
   c) jaded

NEWS FLASH

There is a problem with this news report. The person who wrote it forgot all about punctuation and other rules of writing! Can you help correct this piece so that readers are able to make sense of it?

The Daily News

it is reported this afternoon that two of the thieves who robbed mrsstrangeway's house on monday night have been caught by the police they had not left the district the third man ran away and escaped the police have a full description of him he is stout tall and has a moustache and red hair unfortunately the stolen articles have not yet been recovered anyone having seen a man of the above description is asked to contact the police

PICTURE CLUES

You are Mrs Strangeway and the police have asked you for pictures of the stolen objects. Draw them in the space provided below.

TIMMY'S MISSING!

CHAPTER SIXTEEN

Excerpt from *Five Are Together Again*

'George, can't you sit still for even a minute!' said Julian. 'It's bad enough to have the train rocking about all over the place, without you falling over my feet all the time, going to look out of first one window and then the other.'

'Well, we're nearly at Kirrin – almost home!' said George. 'I can't help feeling excited. I've missed old Timmy so much this term, and I just can't wait to see him! I love to look out of the window and see how much nearer we are to Kirrin. Do you think Timmy will be on the station to meet us, barking madly?'

'Don't be an ass,' said Dick. 'He's a clever dog, but not clever enough to read railway timetables.'

'He doesn't need to,' said George. 'He always knows when I'm coming home.'

'I really believe he does,' said Anne, seriously. 'Your mother always says how excited he is on the day you are arriving home from school – can't keep still – keeps going to the front gate and looking down the road.'

'Dear, dear Timmy!' said George, falling over Julian's feet again, as she scrambled once more to the window. 'We're nearly there. Look, there's the signal-box, and the signal is down. HURRAH!'

Her three cousins looked at her in amusement. George was always like this on the way home from school. Her thoughts were full of very little else but her beloved Timmy all the way home. Julian thought how much she looked like a restless boy just then, with her short, curly hair, and her determined expression. George had always longed to be a boy, but as she wasn't, she made up for it by trying to speak and act like one, and would never answer to her full name of Georgina.

'We're coming into Kirrin station!' yelled George, almost falling out of the window. 'I can see our porter. Hey, Peters – we're back again. WE'RE BACK AGAIN!'

The train slid into Kirrin station, and Peters waved and grinned. He had known George since she was a baby. George opened the door and leapt out of the carriage.

'Home again! Back at Kirrin! Oh, I do hope Timmy will be at the station!' she said.

But there was no Timmy there. 'He must have forgotten you were coming,' said Dick, with a grin, and at once got a scowl from George. Peters came up, smiling all over his face, and gave them his usual welcome. Everyone in Kirrin Village knew the Five – which, of course, included Timmy the dog.

Peters soon had the children's luggage out, and

wheeled it down the platform on his trolley. 'I'll send it along to Kirrin Cottage as soon as the van comes,' he said. 'Had a good term?'

'Smashing!' said Dick. 'But it seemed very long, as Easter is so late this year. My word – look at the primroses on the railway banks.'

But George had no eyes for anything just then. She was still looking out for Timmy. Where was he? WHY hadn't he come to the station to meet them? He came last time and the time before! She turned a troubled face to Dick.

'Do you think he's ill?' she asked. 'Or has he forgotten me? Or…'

'Oh, don't be an ass, George,' said Dick. 'He is probably in the house somewhere and can't get out. Look out – the trolley nearly ran you over then.'

George skipped out of the way, glaring. WHERE was Timmy? She was sure he was ill – or had had an accident – or was tied up and couldn't get away. Perhaps Joan, the cook, had forgotten to let him loose.

'I'm going to take a taxi home, if I've enough money,' she said, taking out her purse. 'You others can walk. I must see if anything's happened to Timmy – he's never missed meeting our train before.'

'But George, it's such a lovely walk to Kirrin Cottage!' said Anne. 'You know how you love to see your island – dear old Kirrin Island – as we walk to your mother's house – and the bay – and hear the waves crashing on the rocks.'

'I'm taking the station taxi,' said George, obstinately, counting the money in her purse. 'If you'd like to come with me, you can. It's Timmy I want to see, not islands and waves and things! I'm sure he's ill or has had an accident or something!'

'All right, George, do as you please,' said Julian. 'Hope you find dear old Timmy is perfectly well – and has only forgotten the time of the train. See you later.'

The two brothers, and their sister Anne, set off together, looking forward to the walk to Kirrin Cottage. How lovely to see Kirrin Bay again, and George's island!

'Isn't she lucky to have a real island of her very own!' said Anne. 'Fancy it belonging to her family for years and years – and then one day her mother suddenly gives it to George! I bet she worried and worried dear Aunt Fanny until she gave in to old George. I do so hope Timmy is all right; we shan't enjoy our holidays with George's mother if there's anything wrong with Timmy.'

'Oh, George will probably go and live in Timmy's kennel with him,' said Dick, with a chuckle. 'Ha – look! The sea – and Kirrin Bay – AND the little old island as lovely as ever!'

'With its gulls circling round, and mewing like cats,' said Julian. 'And the old ruined castle there, just exactly the same as usual. Not a single stone fallen out of it, as far as I can see.'

'You can't possibly see that at this distance,' said Anne, screwing up her eyes. 'Oh, isn't the first day of the hols heavenly? We seem to have all the time in the world in front of us!'

'Yes. And then, alas, after a few days, the holidays rush by,' said Julian. 'I wonder if George is home by now.'

'Well, her taxi passed us going at a tremendous pace!' said Dick. 'I bet old George was shouting at the driver to go as fast as possible!'

'Look – there's Kirrin Cottage – I can just see the chimneys in the distance,' said Dick. 'Smoke is coming from one of them.'

'Funny – why only one?' said Julian. 'They usually have the kitchen fire going, and a fire in Uncle Quentin's study. He's such a cold mortal when he's working out all his wonderful figures for his inventions.'

'Perhaps he's away,' said Anne, hopefully. She was

rather afraid of George's hasty-tempered father. 'I should think Uncle Quentin could do with a holiday at times – he's always buried in rows and rows of figures.'

'Well, let's hope we don't disturb him too much,' said Julian. 'It's hard on Aunt Fanny if he keeps yelling at everyone. We'll try and be out of doors most of the time.'

They were nearly at Kirrin Cottage now. As they came near to the front gate, they saw George come running down the garden path. To Julian's horror, she was crying bitterly.

'I say – it does look as if something has happened to old Timmy,' he said, scared. 'It's not like George to cry – she never cries! What can have happened?'

COMPREHENSION CHECK!

Q What kind of school do the children go to if they are able to come home only for the holidays?

Q Do you think George is right when she says Timmy knows when she's going to be home? How do you think Timmy comes to know?

Q Why does Anne think George's father could do with a vacation?

Q Why do you think George wants to be a boy?

Q What do you think Julian means when he describes his uncle as a 'cold mortal'?

Q What kind of a job do you think Uncle Quentin does? Why?

THINK OF ANOTHER WORD

The train *slid* into Kirrin station. Can you think of another word or phrase that might describe the action of a train arriving at a station? (For example, the train *groaned* into Kirrin station). Write the sentence again with the new word/phrase.

And, *alas*, after a few days, the holidays rush by. Think of another word for alas.

Well, her taxi passed us, going at a *tremendous* pace. Think of another word for tremendous.

'Dear, dear Timmy!' said George, falling over Julian's feet again, as she *scrambled* once more to the window. Think of another word for scrambled.

MORE THAN JUST A FEELING!

George and her cousins feel excitement, anticipation, anxiety and impatience as they approach Kirrin. Pull out one sentence each from the excerpt that reflects those emotions or moods.

Excitement:

Anticipation:

Anxiety:

Impatience:

HAPPY HOLIDAYS

Can you imagine living on an island? Think of five ways by which you'd spend time in the holidays. Remember you're living in Enid Blyton's time! There's no TV and no Internet.

1. ____________________

2. ____________________

3. ____________________

4. ____________________

5. ____________________

CHANGING PERSPECTIVE!

A *first-person narrative* is when you read or listen to a story as told from the narrator's point of view. The narrator is the 'I' in the story. This excerpt you just read uses the *third-person narrative*, or the author's voice. It is rare, but not unheard of, to read a story in the *second-person narrative.* Here, the author talks to her reader like she herself is a spectator, or like she is talking to another person in the story. A second-person narrator uses 'you', 'your' and 'you are' to tell the story.

1. 'George, can't you sit still for even a minute!' said Julian. 'It's bad enough to have the train rocking about all over the place, without you falling over my feet all the time, going to look out of first one window and then the other.'

   Write this sentence from Julian's point of view.

2. George skipped out of the way, glaring. WHERE was Timmy? She was sure he was ill – or had had an accident – or was tied up and couldn't get away. Perhaps Joan, the cook, had forgotten to let him loose.

Write this sentence from George's point of view.

3. The train slid into Kirrin station, and Peters waved and grinned. He had known George since she was a baby. George opened the door and leapt out of the carriage.

Write this sentence from the second-person point of view.

A CAR RIDE

CHAPTER SEVENTEEN

Excerpt from *Five Go to Demon's Rocks*

Once they were out on the main road, Tinker began to talk to the driver, asking him questions about all kinds of cars. The others listened, amused.

'Well, I don't think much of the new cars,' said Tinker. 'All gadgets!'

'Some of the new gadgets are very good,' said the driver, amused with the cocky little boy, and he touched a little lever beside him. At once the window next to Tinker went down smoothly, with a curious low moan. Tinker was extremely startled.

'Oh, don't open that window,' said Anne, as a

rough wind swooped in. 'For goodness' sake, shut it, Tinker.'

Tinker shut it and began to talk about cars again. Once more the driver touched the lever beside him, and once more Tinker's window slid mournfully down, and a cold draught came in.

'TINKER! Don't mess about with the windows,' ordered Julian.

'I never touched the thing,' said Tinker, eyeing the window with suspicion. It suddenly shut itself, sliding upwards very smoothly. Tinker began to feel uncomfortable. He watched the window closely, afraid that it might play tricks again. The others, knowing perfectly well that the driver could open and shut any of the windows automatically from his own seat, nudged one another, and giggled.

'That shut up poor old Tinker!' murmured Dick.

It had. Not another word about new cars or old came from Tinker during the whole drive! It was a very pleasant one, mostly round the coast, and very little inland. The views were magnificent.

'That dog of yours seems to like the views,' said the driver. 'His head has been out of the window all the time.'

'Well – I always thought it was because he liked the fresh air,' said George. 'Timmy, is it because you enjoy the views?'

'Woof,' said Timmy, and withdrew his head to give George a lick. He also gave the little monkey a lick. Poor Mischief didn't much like the motion of the car. He sat very still, indeed, afraid that he might be sick. The car purred along, sounding just like Tinker's usual imitation!

They stopped for an early lunch, and ate their sandwiches hungrily, sitting on a cliff. The driver had brought his own, and once Mischief had discovered that half the man's sandwiches were made of tomato, he sat on his knee in a very friendly manner, sharing his sandwiches in delight.

'We'll be there in another hour or so,' said the man. 'Where are you staying at Demon's Rocks? The garage didn't tell me.'

'At the lighthouse,' said Julian. 'Do you know it?'

'Yes – but people don't stay there!' said the driver, thinking that Julian was pulling his leg. 'What hotel are you going to – or are you staying with friends?'

'No. We really are going to the lighthouse,' said Tinker. 'It's mine. My very own.'

'Well – you've certainly got a place with a fine view!' said the driver. 'I was born at Demon's Rocks. My old great-grandad is still in the same cottage where I was born. My word – the stories he used to tell me of that old lighthouse – and how the wreckers got into it one night and grabbed the keeper there, and doused the light, so that a great ship might go on the rocks.'

'How horrible – and did it get wrecked?' asked Dick.

'Yes. Smashed to bits,' said the driver. 'Ab-sol-utely – smashed – to bits! And then they waited for the tide to wash up the wreckage. You ought to look up my old great-grandad, and get him to tell you his tales. He might even show you the Wreckers' Cave…'

'Oh – we heard about that,' said George. 'Is it really true – can we see it? And is there someone in there still?'

'No – no, all the old wreckers are gone long ago,' said the driver. 'As soon as the new lighthouse was built, the wreckers' day was done. It's so powerful, you see. Its beams can be seen even in the fiercest storm. The beam from the lighthouse you're going to wasn't very good – but it saved a good many ships, all the same!'

'What's your grandad's name?' asked George, making up her mind to look him up as soon as she could. 'Where does he live?'

'Ask for Jeremiah Boogie,' said the driver, carefully skirting a herd of cows. 'You'll find him sitting somewhere on the quay, smoking a long pipe, and scowling at anyone that comes nigh him. But he likes children, so don't you be afraid of his scowl. He'll tell you a few tales, will my old great-grandad! Well, bless us all, if there isn't another herd of cows coming round the corner.'

'Hoot at them,' said Tinker.

'Ever heard the rhyme about the cow that jumped over the moon, boy?' said the driver. 'Well, someone hooted when it came by, see? And that's what it did – jumped over the moon! No good driver hoots at cows. It scares them silly, and they jump like hares. Look – see that cliff round the curve of the coast there? Well, that's the first bit of Demon's Rocks. We'll soon be there now.'

'Why is it called that?' asked George.

'Well, the rocks there are so wicked that it was reckoned they could only have been put there by some kind of savage demon,' said the driver. 'Some are just below the water so that they catch the keel of a boat and rip it. Others stick up sharp as sharks' teeth – and there's a great ledge of rocks where a boat can be pounded to bits by the waves. Ah, they're Demon's Rocks all right!'

'When shall we see the lighthouse?' asked Tinker. 'We ought to see it soon.'

'Wait till another bit of the coast comes in sight as soon as we get to the top of this hill,' said the driver. 'And just tell that monkey of yours to take his paw out of my coat pocket. I've no more tomatoes there!'

'Behave yourself, Mischief,' said Tinker, so sternly that the little creature hid its face in its paws and whimpered.

'Little humbug!' said George. 'There's not a tear in his eye! Oh look – is that the lighthouse?'

'Yes. That's it,' said the driver. 'You get a good view of it now, from this hill. Fine one isn't it, for an old one? Ah, they could build well in those days. That one's made of stone. It's wave-swept so it has to be fairly tall, or the shining of the lamp would have been hidden by the spray falling on the windows.'

'Where did the lighthouse keeper live?' asked Dick.

'Oh, there's a cosy enough room just under the lamp room,' said the driver. 'My grandad took me up there once. I never saw such a view of a stormy sea in my life!'

'My father lived there all one summer,' boasted Tinker. 'I was with him most of the time. It was grand.'

'Why did your father want to live in a lighthouse?' asked the driver, curiously. 'Was he hiding, or something?'

'Of course not. He's a scientist, and he said he wanted peace and quiet, with no telephones ringing, and no one coming to see him,' said Tinker.

'And do you mean to say he had peace and quiet with you there?' said the driver teasingly. 'Well, well!'

'It's not so quiet there really,' said Tinker. 'The waves make such a noise, and so does the wind. But my father didn't really notice those. He only notices things like bells ringing, or people talking, or somebody knocking at the door. Things like that drive him mad. He loved the lighthouse.'

'Well – I hope you enjoy yourselves there,' said the driver. 'It's not my cup of tea – hearing nothing but waves and gulls crying. Better you than me!'

COMPREHENSION CHECK!

Q Do you think the driver likes children? What makes you think so?

Q How many people and animals are there in the car?

Q What is the rhyme about the cow jumping over the moon that the driver talks about?

Q **What is the purpose of a lighthouse?**

Q **Why do you think Tinker's father is bothered by noises in his house but not the ones in the lighthouse?**

This story is set near the sea. Write down five words from the excerpt that tell you about the setting.

Make sentences with the following words.

SUSPICION:

NUDGED:

WHIMPER:

MAGNIFICENT:

IMITATION:

BLOWING IN THE WIND

A strong wind blew when the driver was telling this story and carried away some of his words. Fill in the missing words.

> 'Well, the rocks there are so ___________ that it was ___________ they could only have been put there by some kind of ___________,' said the driver. 'Some are just below the ___________ so that they catch the _________ of a boat and _________ it. Others stick up sharp as sharks' teeth – and there's a great ___________ of rocks where a boat can be ___________ to bits by the waves. Ah, they're Demon's Rocks all right!'

The same wind blew all of the punctuation marks away when Tinker was talking about his father's stay in the lighthouse. Find them and fix them in place. Also, correct the spellings!

> Its not so quiet there really said Tinker the waves make such a noise and so does the wind but my father didnt really notice those he only notices things like bells ringing or people talking or somebody knocking at the door things like that drive him mad he loved the lighthouse

Uh oh. We made some spelling mistakes when we were trying to write this para out for you. Your sharp sleuth eyes will find them, we're sure!

> 'Ever heard the rime about the cow that jumpped over the moon, boy?' said the driver. 'Well, someone huted when it

came by, see? And that's what it did – jumped over the muin! No good driver hootts at cows. It skares them silly, and they jump like hairs. Look – see that clif round the curve of the cost there? Well, thar's the first bit of Demon's Rocks. We'll soon be their now.'

ANSWERS

Please note: This section has answers to the fill in the blanks, match the following, true or false, word jumble and crossword exercises. Answers to questions on comprehension, making sentences, character sketches, synonyms and antonyms have not been provided since they may vary from child to child depending on the reading of the text, possibility of multiple answers or the creative nature of the task.

Chapter 1: It's a Mystery
Answers to the exercises on Page 8

A. Wrong
B. Wrong
C. Right
D. Wrong

a. stern
b. oars
c. hull
d. bow

Chapter 2: Scamper and Timmy Make Mischief
Answers to Match the Following

Scamper → excited
Mischief → naughty
Julian → respectful
Professor → forgetful
Tinker → exasperated

Chapter 3: Gone Missing!

Here is Elizabeth's description corrected:

Elizabeth can be recognized by her mass of soft, dark, curly hair, her *brown* eyes, straight eyebrows, and scar down *one arm*. She is *tall* for her age, and strong. She *swims well and is fond of horses.*

Answers to the exercise on Page 25

a. a missing girl
b. stolen money
c. the scar on her arm
d. they'd know where a young girl may hide better than grown-ups would
e. she wouldn't know what to say to her

Answers to Crossword Fun

Across

1. tenant
2. resolved
3. thinking about
4. shed
5. deserted

Down

1. disagreement
2. debate
3. blame
4. completely
5. thicket

P	Q	R	S	D	P	Q	R	S	T	P	Q	R	S	T	P	R	R	S
Q	R	S	T	I	P	Q	R	S	T	Q	R	S	T	T	P	Q	R	S
R	S	D	E	S	E	R	T	E	D	R	S	S	S	T	P	Q	R	Q
S	T	P	S	A	P	Q	R	S	T	S	T	P	S	T	P	Q	R	S
P	Q	R	S	G	P	Q	R	S	T	P	Q	R	T	E	N	A	N	T
Q	R	S	T	R	P	Q	R	S	T	P	R	S	H	P	Q	S	T	P
R	S	S	S	E	P	Q	R	S	T	P	S	T	I	P	R	S	T	T
S	T	T	S	E	P	Q	R	S	D	P	T	R	C	P	Q	R	S	H
T	P	Q	R	M	P	Q	S	H	E	D	Q	R	K	P	R	S	T	I
P	Q	R	S	E	P	Q	R	S	B	P	C	P	E	P	Q	R	S	N
Q	R	S	T	N	Q	S	T	T	A	S	O	P	T	P	T	R	S	K
R	S	T	P	T	P	Q	R	S	T	P	M	P	Q	R	R	S	P	I
S	T	P	S	T	Q	B	P	Q	E	P	P	Q	R	S	S	T	Q	N
T	P	Q	S	P	R	L	P	Q	R	S	L	R	S	T	T	T	R	G
P	Q	R	S	T	S	A	P	Q	R	S	E	S	T	P	Q	R	S	A
Q	R	S	S	T	T	M	P	Q	R	S	T	T	P	Q	R	S	T	B
R	S	T	S	T	R	E	S	O	L	V	E	D	Q	R	S	T	P	O
S	T	R	S	T	P	Q	R	S	T	P	L	P	R	S	P	Q	R	U
T	P	Q	R	T	P	Q	R	S	T	P	Y	P	S	T	Q	R	S	T

Chapter 4: An Important Meeting
Answers to the word puzzle on Page 36

M	A	S	C	I	E	N	T	I	S	T	O	E	K
O	M	D	B	K	O	O	B	C	I	M	O	C	D
G	C	I	F	I	C	A	P	S	P	R	H	A	Y
O	W	L	E	O	N	A	R	D	Q	U	I	E	T
S	C	N	A	D	S	E	T	L	E	H	B	S	I
E	A	D	V	A	I	E	R	J	S	H	I	P	S
D	D	O	D	T	Y	P	A	O	O	O	G	E	R
C	Y	E	S	K	N	R	N	A	L	W	B	A	E
E	N	S	E	C	C	E	Q	N	N	A	A	C	V
A	P	E	R	N	Y	H	U	E	G	R	N	E	I
Z	T	I	E	O	L	O	I	T	H	O	G	F	N
E	C	N	N	I	C	S	L	N	C	T	N	U	U
A	G	R	E	P	Y	S	H	E	L	D	O	L	P
E	E	N	T	S	T	I	L	L	N	T	I	S	T

Chapter 5: Fit to Be King!
Answers to Mad Scramble

A. Fatty was preparing himself very earnestly for Tuesday night. He knew how important it was, and he also knew that, unless all his details were absolutely perfect, he might be in considerable danger.

B. He tried to memorize exactly at what angle Napoleon wore his hat, exactly how he held his hands, exactly how he stared so blankly in front of him.

C. It was a very bold idea indeed. Not one of the other Find-Outers would have dared to do it. But Fatty, of course, would dare anything. Bets thought that he wouldn't even turn a hair if he met a roaring lion, the kind she met in her bad dreams, and which scared her terribly.

Answers to Word Jumble

medals, dreams, memorize, clothes, safety, tummy, brainy

Enid Blyton did not write history, or chemistry, or anything about geometry or trigonometry. But she could certainly write a good MYSTERY!

Chapter 7: A Feast for Five
Answers to the exercise on Page 57

a) Whistling
b) Tobogganing
c) Exclaiming
d) Melting
e) Sliding

Chapter 8: A New Girl
Answers to the exercise on Page 64

a) distinctly
b) expectantly

Answers to the exercises on Page 65

a) Isabel
b) Mam'zelle
c) Susan
d) Claudine

École
Ami
Prof
Fille
Nièce

Chapter 9: The Wailing Violin
Answers to Crooked Connections

A	B	C
mournful	joyful	sad
ignorance	knowledge	innocence
silent	noisy	quiet
carefully	carelessly	watchfully
arrived	departed	reached
strange	ordinary	curious
crying	laughing	sobbing

Answers to Who Says These Lines?

a) Peter
b) Jack
c) George
d) Peter

Answers to the exercise on Page 74

a) banjo
b) pram
c) shack
d) town

Chapter 10: A Riding Accident
Answers to Who Are They?

Jim – the stable boy

Patsy and Rose – two girls from the second form
Thunder – the horse
Bill – riding instructor
Miss Peters – teacher

Chapter 11: A Job for Timmy
Answers to the exercise on Page 88

a) some small animal
b) such a peculiar house
c) absolutely empty and quiet
d) in the big fireplace
e) he carried the lamp

Chapter 13: A Quarrel, and a Picnic!
Answers to What Comes First

1. Timothy finds a ball to play with.
2. George and Wilfrid have an argument.
3. Julian breaks up the quarrel between George and Wilfrid.
4. Anne and Dick get lunch ready.
5. Dick thinks Wilfrid is badly brought up.
6. Dick breaks a glass.
7. A magpie steals Wilfrid's tomato and flies away.
8. Everyone notices that boats don't seem to go anywhere near Whispering Islands.

Answers to Sharp-eyed Sleuth

1. George *grabbed* the dog's collar, and aimed a punch at the whistling boy. (caught hold)
2. George looked round at him *angrily* and he made a face at her. (furiously)
3. You take on *all the responsibility* and we just let you! (everything on your shoulders)

4. The magpie put its *shiny* head on one side and chattered back to him in bird-language. (glossy)
5. It was lovely sitting up on the hillside, watching the boats in the harbour, and seeing the beautiful, white-sailed yachts bending t*his way and that way* in the strong wind that blew there. (to and fro)

Answers to Spot the Differences

1. Julian's t-shirt does not have a logo.
2. There are no stones on the ground.
3. Julian is not holding a cookie.
4. There is a notebook on the floor.
5. Dick is wearing socks.

Chapter 14: Everyone's Angry with Prudence
Answers to Show Time
Circus

Chapter 15: Who's the Guy
Answers to What's That Word Again?

1. dismayed
2. unfortunate
3. peculiar
4. jolly

Answers to News Flash

It is reported this afternoon that two of the thieves who robbed Mrs Strangeway's house on Monday night have been caught by the police. They had not left the district. The third man ran away and escaped. The police have a full description of him. He is stout, tall and has a moustache and red hair. Unfortunately, the stolen articles have not yet been recovered. Anyone having seen a man of the above description is asked to contact the police.

Chapter 16: Timmy's Missing!
Answers to Changing Perspective!

1. 'George, can't you sit still for even a minute!' I said. 'It's bad enough to have the train rocking about all over the place, without you falling over my feet all the time, going to look out of first one window and then the other.'
2. I skipped out of the way, glaring. WHERE was Timmy? I was sure he was ill – or had had an accident – or was tied up and couldn't get away. Perhaps Joan, the cook, had forgotten to let him loose.
3. The train slid into Kirrin station, and you waved and grinned. You had known George since she was a baby. George opened the door and leapt out of the carriage.

Chapter 17: A Car Ride
Answers to Blowing in the Wind

'Well, the rocks there are so wicked that it was reckoned they could only have been put there by some kind of savage demon,' said the driver. 'Some are just below the water so that they catch the keel of a boat and rip it. Others stick up sharp as sharks' teeth – and there's a great ledge of rocks where a boat can be pounded to bits by the waves. Ah, they're Demon's Rocks all right!'

'It's not so quiet there really,' said Tinker. 'The waves make such a noise, and so does the wind. But my father didn't really notice those. He only notices things like bells ringing, or people talking, or somebody knocking at the door. Things like that drive him mad. He loved the lighthouse.'

'Ever heard the rhyme about the cow that jumped over the moon, boy?' said the driver. 'Well, someone hooted when it came by, see? And that's what it did – jumped over the moon! No good driver hoots at cows. It scares them silly, and they jump like hares. Look – see that cliff round the curve of the coast there? Well, that's the first bit of Demon's Rocks. We'll soon be there now.'

9789351952619